FIELD AND LABORATORY MICROBIAL ECOLOGY

FIELD AND LABORATORY MICROBIAL ECOLOGY

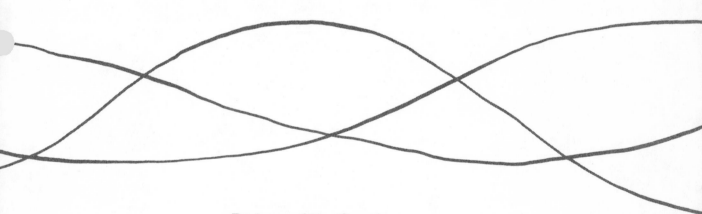

Robert W. Gorden

Southern Colorado State College

WM. C. BROWN COMPANY PUBLISHERS
Dubuque, Iowa

Contents

Preface vii

I. Introduction 1

    1. Plate Counting Methods 3
    2. Measurement of Microorganism Populations by Direct Methods 7
    3. ATP and Its Ecological Significance 13
    4. Enrichment Culture of *Acinetobacter* 19

II. Ecological Succession 23

    5. The Use of Microcosms 27
    6. Community Structure and Pigment Ratio 33
    7. Dominant Bacterial Types 39

IIII. Ecological Functions of Microorganisms 43

IV. The Use of Radioactive Substrates in Microbial Ecology 45

    8. The Use of Carbon-14 in the Measurement of Primary Productivity in Aquatic Habitats 47
    9. Measurement of "Heterotrophic Potential" of Aquatic Bacteria Using Radioactive Substrates 51
    10. Capture of CO_2 Respired by Heterotrophs in Aquatic Systems 55
    11. Autoradiographic Methods 59
    12. Tracer Techniques in Nutrient Cycling 65

V. Ecological Energy Flow 71

    13. The Measurement of Standing Crop Biomass 73
    14. Radioactive Tracer Studies 81
    15. Growth in Filtrate of Other Cultures 85
    16. Losses from Phytoplankton to Consumers 89
    17. Nematodes on Fungal Mats 93

VI. Community Metabolism and Decomposition Studies 97

    18. Measurement of Community Metabolism 99
    19. Carbon Dioxide Evolution by Soil Communities 103

20. The Living Sediment 107
21. The Use of Litter Bags to Measure Decomposition of
    Natural Substrates 111
22. A Litter Bag Method: Decomposition in Aquatic Systems . . 115
23. Decomposition of Unconfined Substrates 119
24. Decomposition of Dissolved Organic Materials 123

VII. Eutrophication, Ecology and Pollution Control 125

25. Chemostats as Ecological Tools, Continuous Culture of
    Bacteria 127
26. Measurement of Nitrogen Fixation by Soil and Aquatic
    Microorganisms 133
27. Bacterial Utilization of ^{32}P 139

Appendix I

Microorganisms and Humans 145
Rumen Microbial Ecology 146

Appendix II

Phosphate Determinations 149
Bomb Calorimetry 152
Seawater in the Laboratory 157
Oxygen Determinations 159

Recommended Reading 161

References 163

Preface

Field and Laboratory Microbial Ecology was originally designed, written and used for a one semester, graduate level course in Microbial Ecology.

This manual is suitable for use in courses in aquatic and soil microbiology, limnology and general ecology. Specific exercises may be incorporated into the laboratory sequence of Honors Biology and independent study courses.

All exercises are open-ended, flexible and require a limited amount of supervision. Most of the materials and equipment suggested are commonly available in Biology and Chemistry laboratories. Few exercises require expensive equipment.

The ecological concepts coincide with the exercises of that section. They are included as an aid to students and instructors with limited ecological training.

The manual was written with two objectives: (1) to encourage others to develop courses in the interesting and productive area of the ecology of microorganisms, and (2) to stimulate new approaches and to contribute to the quality of research in microbial ecology.

My thanks are extended to Drs. Dennis Cooke and Robert Johannes who offered suggestions on the manuscript. The manual was written while the author was a member of the Biology Department of Texas Tech University. The use of materials, equipment and personnel of that department in the preparation of the manuscript is deeply appreciated.

Comments and suggestions regarding the content and approach of the manual will be appreciated.

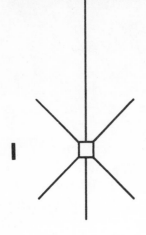

I

Introduction

This laboratory manual is written as an invitation for you to gain an understanding of the function of microorganisms in nature. It provides open-ended exercises which will enable you to use the techniques and methods in many types of natural systems.

In microbial ecology one is interested in functions and interactions of the microbial populations of an ecosystem. Specifically, you will be asked to find the answer or a part of the answer to such questions as these:

1. What are the cells doing in the environment?
2. How do they contribute to the capacity of the community to respond to stress and perturbations, whether natural or man made?
3. Can the cellular function change (do the cells use other metabolic pathways) as the habitat changes?
4. What are the interactions between groups which dampen oscillations and fluctuations of population numbers, increase species diversity and thereby contribute to the development of a mature, stable community?
5. What are the contributions to energy flow, nutrient cycling and to the food web made by the microbial populations in the community?

As you seek answers to these questions some of the tools and skills you have learned in the past will be useful, as well as those you will be gaining from these laboratory exercises. Look for new approaches, think through your ideas and make contributions to the lab. The entire course is designed to give you a better understanding of what microorganisms *do* in nature.

Rather than separating a species from the community, isolating it in pure culture, and observing morphological and physiological characteristics under laboratory conditions, the goal of the microbial ecologist is to learn to make astute and refined observations in nature. The use of modern equipment and methods now allows us to make studies of natural habitats which previously were impossible. Field studies may then be supplemented by laboratory experiments under controlled conditions. Microbial function may be determined by using classical and modern equipment and methods in *in vivo* and *in vitro* situations. The suggestion offered here is that these methods be used as a means to an ecological end.

The first section of the manual consists of exercises in which quantitative methods useful in microbial ecology are outlined. These methods and techniques are intended to supplement those which you have used previously for other laboratory studies. In the following sections procedures for observing microbial function in the laboratory and in nature are emphasized. Included in the introductions to each section are brief discussions of ecological interest.

Instructors and students using this manual are encouraged to adapt these exercises to various ecological studies.[1] The author will appreciate discussion and criticism regarding the content and approaches presented.

1. An understanding of the fundamental principles and concepts of microbiology and ecology will be most helpful for those students interested in getting the best information from this relatively specialized course.

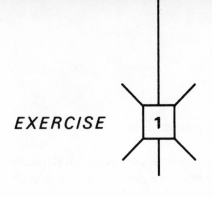
The plate count methods which you have used include the dilution pour plate method. You are aware of the problems and deficiencies of the pour plate method; also, remember the values: (1) a relative count can be made of viable bacteria capable of growth with the agar and incubation conditions being used; (2) the growth of the bacterial colonies on and in the agar are characteristic of the species or type; and (3) this method allows one to observe different colony morphological types, chromogenic characteristics and dominant bacterial types.

A. Substrate Variation

Modifications of the dilution pour plate methods are many and are limited only by the ingenuity of the investigator. The capacity of bacteria in natural systems to grow on a particular substrate may be determined by incorporating that substrate in the agar as the sole carbon source. When various substrates are used the agar base choice is Noble agar or some other rigorously cleaned and purified agar. Control plates containing Noble agar only as a carbon source should be used to compare the number of bacteria growing on *agar only* with those growing on the substrate. Sole carbon sources used may include insecticides, herbicides and other pesticides, cellulose, chitin and other difficult-to-decompose substances. A long incubation period may be necessary to allow substantial growth of the colonies.

Bacterial isolates from the ocean may be capable of using crude or purified alginic acid as a sole carbon source. Such bacteria will often degrade agar and alginic acid leaving a pit or hole in the agar. Another modification of the dilution plate method consists of placing the dilution sample *on the agar surface* and spreading the sample using a sterile bent glass rod. Microorganisms which require aerobic growth conditions may thus be able to grow on the surface but not in the agar. Adjustment of the agar to a pH range at which the selected organisms may grow is of great importance. With pesticides, a series of plates involving a wide range of concentration of the substrate should be employed.

B. Anaerobic Types

The following exercise may be useful when selecting microaerophilic, facultative and strict anaerobic bacteria. The procedure makes use of the replica plating technique developed in bacterial genetics studies (Lederberg and Lederberg, 1952). Since many bacteria are capable of growing aerobically or anaerobically, one may wish to select obligate anaerobes and exclude facultative anaerobes.

MATERIALS

Anaerobic plate covers, sterilized
Anaerobic jar
Brewer anaerobic agar or equivalent
Ointment jars or pistons
Squares of velveteen
Petri plates, sterilized
Spreading rods
Dilution bottles
Pipets, 1.1 ml
Nutrient agar, Noble agar, specific agar

3

PROCEDURE

1. Take a natural soil sample or water sample and follow the dilution procedure.
2. Make nutrient agar plates using Brewer drying lids.
3. Place aliquots of each dilution on duplicate nutrient agar plates and also on duplicate anaerobic agar plates. Spread each type of plate using a separate sterile glass rod for each plate. Carefully spread the anaerobic plate sample within the area covered by the Brewer lid.
4. Incubate the anaerobic plates in an anaerobic jar or in a CO_2 incubator. Incubate the aerobic plates in an aerobic incubator. Incubation temperature is dependent upon the habitat being studied.
5. Check the plates within 2 days. If growth on the anaerobic plates is slow allow another day before proceeding. Colonies must grow to a suitable diameter (pinhead or larger) prior to carrying out the following steps.

Microbial growth under anaerobic conditions indicated the use of a metabolic pathway for nonaerobic growth. However, such growth does not preclude the presence of an aerobic pathway.

6. Attach the velveteen squares smoothly to the cap of the ointment jars or pistons and tie in place with string or wire. (Rubber bands will not withstand autoclaving.) Check to see if the piston and velveteen will fit inside a petri plate (bottom section). Sterilize the piston and the attached velveteen inside a closed paper bag or wrapped in paper.
7. Prepare two agar plates for each anaerobic agar plate. One sterile piston for each plate to be transferred will also be needed.
8. Select a dilution plate containing 20-100 distinct colonies on both anaerobic and aerobic plates.
9. Mark and position the plates. To make a replica plate touch the sterile velveteen-piston lightly to the anaerobic plate surface and carefully transfer the colonies to the nutrient agar surface. Be certain the piston does not turn in the plate during the transfer. A replicate anaerobic plate may be made at the same time. Incubate these replica plates aerobically; colonies which grow are not obligate aerobes. Colonies which grow only anaerobically *may* obligate anaerobes.
10. A similar process may be carried out by using the aerobic plates from the initial sample and making a transfer to anaerobic plates to determine obligate aerobes.

Note: Use extreme care when handling certain anaerobes because many are killed upon exposure to air. Many laboratories do not have suitable facilities and equipment for the transfer and culture of strict anerobic bacteria.

Questions

1. Suggest methods for comparing other types of growth characteristics using the above methods.
2. How may these procedures be useful for determining "ecological enzymes" of an ecosystem? Might methods similar to those used by microbial geneticists to determine the numbers of mutants in a population be applicable here?
3. Describe situations in which a series of different types of agar media and growth conditions may be used to determine the viable numbers of the heterotrophic bacterial, fungal and actinomycetales populations.
4. What agar do you suggest for the isolation and enumeration of aquatic fungi? of soil Streptomyces? of *Caulobacter* sp.?

DATA SHEET

Plate Counts

Sample	Dilution	Media	Aerobes	Anaerobes	Facultative Anaerobes	Comments

Incubation and growth conditions.

Temperature _____

pH of media _____

Incubation time _____

Actinomycetales populations:

PLATE COUNTING METHODS

Results and Discussion

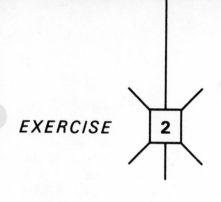
Estimating microbial populations by direct methods has been suggested by several investigators (Strŭgger 1948; Wood 1964). The methods described here may be adapted especially to a particular habitat; modifications may be made which allow the use of these techniques in other situations.

Direct counts of bacteria, algae and fungi are possible using a student light microscope, slides and simple stains. A more refined method involves the use of ultraviolet filters and fluorescent stains. The Wood-Strŭgger acridine-orange method is especially useful for studies of soil and aquatic bacteria. Riva and Turner (1962) have developed a method for nonquantitative tissue study.

A. Fluorescent-Acridine Orange Method, Wood-Strŭgger Modification

OBJECTIVES

To distinguish autotrophic from heterotrophic microorganisms and to obtain a reliable count of each.

MATERIALS AND EQUIPMENT

Light microscope plus light source and UV filters—BG_{12} substage filter and OGl eyepiece filter
Fluorescent or UV microscope
Petroff-Hauser counting chamber and cover slips
Acridine orange stain, 0.01 g/100 ml concentration—maintain under sterile conditions

PROCEDURE

1. Collect and prepare the water or soil sample aseptically.
2. Transfer two 1.0 ml aliquots of the prepared sample to two sterile test tubes.
3. To one of the tubes add 0.5 ml of the acridine orange solution and 0.5 ml of sterile, distilled H_2O resulting in the final dilution of acridine orange being 1:5,000.
4. Record the increased dilution of that sample.
5. Do not add the fluorescent stain to the second sample.
6. The tubes may be mixed on a test tube mixer (Vortex type).
7. Place a well-mixed drop of the sample without acridine orange stain on the Petroff-Hauser chamber and observe using UV light. (Be certain that the protective OGl, yellow eyepiece filter is in place.)
8. It may be necessary to concentrate aquatic (especially marine) microorganisms via centrifugation. This may be accomplished by use of an angle head, table model centrifuge, set at a moderate speed. Dobson and Thomas (1964) suggest the use of a simple suction filtration device which causes little or no damage to microflagellates. The Waring Blender modification of Kimball and Wood (1964) is useful for rapid concentrations of large volumes of sea water.
9. Filtration using 0.3 μ or 0.45 μ membrane filters and a vacuum pressure of 10 psi is suitable for the concentration of most freshwater samples. The correct volume of water to be filtered must be determined empirically.
10. Living autotrophs containing chlorophyll will appear bright red when placed *unstained* on the counting cell under light from the BG_{12} filter. Acridine orange is not necessary since chlorophyll fluoresces red at 450 mμ. Thus, photosynthetic organisms may be counted first.
11. After counting the autotrophs, clean the P-H slide and add a well-mixed drop of the stained sample and proceed to count heterotrophs. Living heterotrophs (without chlorophyll) will

appear green on the field and will contrast with the red of the dead microorganisms and the organic detritus present.

12. Note carefully the detritus particles and the attached bacteria which should be seen clearly.

13. By counting equal dilutions of both stained and unstained samples a comparison of the autotrophic and heterotrophic populations can be made. A total count of the particles seen under ordinary illumination should also be taken. Thus, the ratio between living autotrophs and heterotrophs and total particles can be determined.

14. Directions with the Petroff-Hauser counter will indicate correct counting procedure. (Cells/square $\times$ dilution $\times$ 2×10^7 = cells/ml.) The area formula provided with the P-H counting cell instructions will be dependent upon the sample dilution used which must include the amount of acridine orange present in the aliquot.

15. Record data.

Mechanism of action: Acridine orange is a basic dye and is thought to be absorbed electrostatically by the albuminoid components of living protoplasm. In the concentrations recommended, this is a vital stain.

Cautions: Practice will enable the observer to distinguish movement, size and shape of the heterotrophs. Flagellated invertebrates should be distinguishable from bacteria and fungi. In sea water zooplankton, scales and other organisms or particles of debris may fluoresce red and be difficult to distinguish from phytoplankton.

Dilution or concentration of the sample may be necessary if more or less than 1-10 organisms are present per high power field.

Haemocytometer cells may replace Petroff-Hauser counting chambers as an economy measure in the student laboratory.

B. The Riva-Turner Acridine-Orange Tissue Stain

The Riva-Turner acridine orange method was developed specifically for medical purposes. The method of staining is very rapid (10 seconds) and distinguishes microorganisms from tissue. If bacteria adhere to detritus and/or living cells in vast numbers in water or soil or if they are in clumps and chains, the method may have very little value. Such aggregations may be broken up by agitation in a Waring Blender (water-cooled blender) or similar chopping device. Tween 60, Tween 80 and other surface-acting agents may aid in dispersing clumps of cells.

MATERIALS AND EQUIPMENT

The same equipment used in the Wood-Strügger method.
Additional glassware:
   Pasteur or dilution pipettes
   Three cytology stain jars

PROCEDURE

1. Prepare duplicate slides by spreading a known amount of sample over a given area (0.01 ml spread over 1 cm² area). (The mean of a number of fields may be multiplied by 500,000 to determine the number of cells/ml.) *Do not* fix the slide by heating.

2. Three stain jars containing the following solutions are necessary:
   a. 0.025% acridine orange
   b. 2.0% ethyl alcohol (5.0% isopropyl alcohol)
   c. 0.85% saline (normal saline)

3. Hold the prepared slide by a pair of forceps and agitate the slide vigorously for 3 seconds in the acridine orange, for 3 seconds in the 2% ethyl alcohol and finally for 4 seconds or longer in the normal saline solution.

4. Drain the slides.

5. After staining, the slides may be stored indefinitely.
6. Before examination, slides must be mounted using cover slips and normal saline as a mountant.
7. Slides may be examined under ultraviolet light. Living bacteria, yeast and fungi fluoresce red or reddish-orange. Detritus particles and dead cells stain green or grayish green.
8. This method is especially valuable for rapid screening of atypical animal cells. A further adaptation of this technique involves the enumeration of bacteria associated with wounds or tissue.

Questions

1. Suggest better methods of separating microorganisms from detritus and cellular aggregations.
2. What are the values and problems in the use of surfactants such as Tween 80, Tween 60 and Tepol 6-10?
3. How might an investigator make the most accurate estimates of the biomass of fungi, bacteria and algae of a mixed system?
4. What are the values of having number and biomass estimates of microorganisms in natural habitats? Are there disadvantages to relying on such estimates derived from these methods?

DATA SHEET
Direct Counts

Sample	Dilution	White Light Microscope	Autotrophs	Heterotrophs	Riva-Turner Method

Results and Discussion

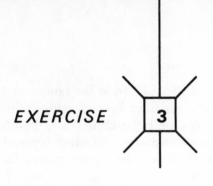

ATP AND ITS
ECOLOGICAL SIGNIFICANCE

The search continues for ways to accurately measure living, functional microorganisms in all types of systems. Microbial ecologists have grown weary of estimating bacterial populations via direct counts and dilution techniques. Although these methods may have value in certain situations it is clear that numbers of microorganisms are of little value if the functions and rates are unknown. In addition, few bacterial species are routinely isolated using typical isolation methods.

What enzymes, amino acids or structural components are: (1) present in all bacteria in equal amounts, (2) unique to bacteria, and (3) relatively easy to measure accurately? To our knowledge no material or group of compounds meets these three requirements. If there are such compounds a fourth criterion must be established, i.e., (4) can the rate of a function be determined by the measurement of the concentration of the compounds? The search goes on!

Bacterial populations of soil, freshwater, air and the sea contain a common component which can be measured. Recent advances have made the measurement of ATP somewhat routine in many laboratories. The component, ATP, does not really meet any of the four criteria proposed. However, measurement of ATP may be a step in the right direction, and this method may yield valuable data.

ATP of the ocean (Holm-Hansen and Booth 1966), of soil (MacLeod, Chappelle and Crawford 1969) and of sewage (Patterson, Brezonik and Putnam 1970) has been measured. It is assumed that below the euphotic zone of the ocean only heterotrophic metabolism is active. In both soil and sewage many other organisms are known to be present. In general, the function in these habitats is, in part, a heterotrophic utilization of organic substrates. By measuring and comparing the amount of ATP with the rates of functions measured separately, ecological information may be extrapolated. Since so many different microorganisms, performing a variety of functions, are present in the habitats described, one must exercise care in the interpretation of these studies.

The ATP-firefly bioluminescence procedure was described by Seliger and McElroy (1960). According to Chapelle and Levin (1968), when ATP and firefly lantern enzyme, luciferase, are combined light is emitted. The total amount of light emitted is a function of the concentrations of luciferase, luciferin, oxygen and ATP. With other components in excess the peak light intensity and total light are directly proportional to the quantity of ATP present in the sample. The emission of light is due to a two step reaction:

$$E + ATP + LH_2 \xrightarrow{Mg++} E - LH_2 - AMP + PP$$

$$E - LH_2 - AMP + O_2 \rightleftharpoons E - L - AMP + H_2O + h_v$$

where:

$$E = \text{enzyme luciferase}$$
$$LH_2 = \text{luciferin (reduced)}$$
$$PP = \text{pyrophosphate}$$
$$L = \text{dehydroluciferin}$$

Certain assumptions must be made when measuring ATP of natural systems:

1. All cells contain ATP.
2. No nonliving particulate material contains ATP.
3. The ratio of ATP to cell carbon is fairly constant.

13

Basically the procedure is dependent upon accurate extraction of the ATP from the sample and precise measurement of the light emitted. Various extraction methods have been developed for specific samples. The procedure outlined below is based on the work of Holm-Hansen and Booth (1966). Light emissions may be measured using a liquid scintillation spectrometer or various types of photomultiplier tubes, power supply amplifier and recorder combinations. (See cited papers for details.)

MATERIALS AND EQUIPMENT

Tris buffer
Firefly luciferase (Sigma Chem. Co.)
ATP standard solution
Sampling equipment for aseptic sampling
Filtering equipment
$0.45\ \mu$ filters
Pasteur pipets
2.0 and 1.0 ml pipets
Calibrated test tubes
Vials, 25×57 mm
Water bath
Centrifuge
Light measuring apparatus
Freezer

PROCEDURE

I. Method of ATP extraction.

1. Filter samples through a $0.45\ \mu$ pore size filter.
2. Place filter immediately in small beaker, 25-30 ml.
3. Add 4.0 ml of boiling Tris buffer (0.2 M, pH 7.75).
4. Place beaker in a boiling water bath for 5 minutes.
5. Transfer solution via sterile Pasteur pipette to a calibrated test tube.
6. Again add 1 or 2 ml of boiling Tris buffer to the beaker with the filter and boil for 2 minutes.
7. Transfer remaining solution to the previous solution in the calibrated test tube, record the volume and freeze at $-25°$C until ready for analysis.

Note: Rapid killing of cells is important to prevent ATP loss.

II. Analysis: Using firefly luciferase as an assay tool.

1. Obtain extracts of firefly lanterns from Sigma Chemical Co. and freeze at $-25°$C until ready for use.
2. Rehydrate 50 mg firefly lantern with 5.0 ml of Tris buffer.
3. Allow suspension to stand at room temperature for 2-3 hours.
4. Centrifuge at $300 \times$ g for 1 minute.
5. Decant to clean, dry test tube and again allow to stand for 30-60 minutes at room temperature.
6. Immediately before use, shake the enzyme preparation and pipette 0.2 ml into a vial (25×57 mm).[1]
7. Shake the vial by hand and read in the light measuring apparatus and record the background light emission.

1. Suggested glass washing procedure to eliminate background light emission Patterson et al. (1970). (1) Soak in hot, soapy wash; (2) Boil 1 hour in acid bath; (3) Triple rinse in deionized, distilled H_2O.

8. To the vial add 0.2 ml of the test solution or an ATP standard solution.
9. Shake vial for 10 seconds to mix solution and read and record.
10. Standardization is important. It is necessary to run an ATP standard assay curve routinely due to variations in the commercial enzyme.

III. Light measuring apparatus.

Patterson et al. (1970) suggest a liquid scintillation spectrometer with a window setting of 50-1000 and the gain set at 53 for light emission measurements.

MacLeod et al. (1969) used an RCA 7265 photomultiplier tube and previously mentioned components.

Holm-Hansen and Booth (1966) used an RCA 6810-A photomultiplier tube and components.

The clever student and instructor can devise a suitable measuring device at a relatively low cost with considerable aid from engineering or physics department personnel.

Questions

1. Does the information gained have ecological value? Explain the ramifications of your answer.
2. Correct the reasoning of investigators who feel that measurements of ATP in sewage, soil and the ocean yield information about bacterial populations.
3. What do you believe is the best use of ATP quantity/unit data?

TO DO

Plot the standard curve. Plot the experimental curves.

DATA SHEET

ATP and Its Ecological Significance

Sample	Source of sample	ATP μ g/unit			Notes
		R_1	R_2	R_3	

Results and Discussion

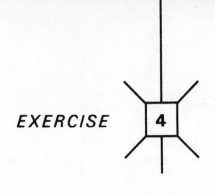
ENRICHMENT CULTURE OF ACINETOBACTER

Enrichment culture methods have been used by those wishing to isolate specific bacterial types from natural habitats. The methods consist of adding soil or water from the habitat to a basal salts solution containing a specific carbon or energy source. During incubation, bacteria capable of utilizing the energy source under the growth conditions imposed should become dominant. These conditions thereby reveal certain ecological capabilities and requirements of the microorganism which may be useful in physiological studies. Based on these selective culture methods, media have been developed which encourage the growth of one metabolic type while excluding other bacteria (See Aaronson 1970).

Baumann (1968) has described an enrichment culture method for the isolation of *Acinetobacter* from soil and water. Previous isolations of *Acinetobacter* have usually been from clinical specimens. This work emphasizes the fact that simple media are not suitable for growth of all bacteria growing in nature. It further stresses the incompleteness of studies which have depended upon substances such as nutrient agar and plate count agar for the enumeration of bacterial populations in nature, and points to a reason why direct counts are usually higher than plate counts.

Acinetobacter was found by Baumann to be a common resident of soil and water. Two main types, oxidase-negative and oxidase-positive, were isolated. The *Acinetobacter* resemble many species of aerobic pseudomonads and it is probable that they function as decomposers of simple carbon compounds at low pH.

MATERIALS AND EQUIPMENT

Medium:
0.2% acetate, (trihydrate)
0.2% KNO_3
0.2% $MgSO_4\,7H_2O$
Hutner's mineral base—20 ml/liter

Make 1 liter using 0.04 M KH_2PO_4 — Na_2HPO_4 (pH6.0) solution

Yeast extract agar and broth
10-125 ml flasks
Rotary Shaker
Whirl-Pak bags or sterile containers
Culture tubes
Culture plates
*Dilution bottles, pipets and procedure, Exercise 1
*Acridine orange direct count procedure, Exercise 2

PROCEDURE

I. Isolation.

1. From natural soil, mud and water habitats aseptically secure samples in sterile containers and return to the laboratory.
2. To each 125 ml flask add 20 ml of *Acinetobacter* media plus 5 ml of water or suspension of soil sample.
3. Label the flask as to the type of inoculum.
4. Incubate at 30°C on a rotary shaker for 48 hours.

5. Direct microscopic observations will indicate whether *Acinetobacter* sp. have developed as dominant organisms.

6. Accurate descriptions of *Acinetobacter* are found in J. Bacteriology 95:1520-1541.

7. Cultures may be streaked on either mineral-acetate or yeast extract agar and later identified on the basis of morphological and physiological properties.

II. Enrichment methods are not quantitative; i.e., accurate estimates of bacterial populations are not possible. Approximate numbers of *Acinetobacter* cells in soil and water samples may be determined using the method briefly described here.

Two series of 6-250 ml flasks should be prepared:

1. To series 1 add 100 ml of *Acinetobacter* enrichment medium and label the flasks 10 ml, 1 ml, 10^1, 10^2, 10^3, 10^4.

2. To series 2 add 100 ml of yeast extract broth and label in the same manner.

3. Make serial dilutions of the sample liquid and inoculate each flask of each series with the appropriate inoculum.

4. Incubate all flasks on a rotary shaker for 48 hours at 30°C.

5. Following incubation make direct counts to determine the numbers of bacteria present.
   a. Acridine orange method may be the most useful method.
   b. Simple stains may also be acceptable.

6. A comparison of the total bacterial count in yeast extract broth with the total count in acetate medium will yield the percentage of *Acinetobacter* present in the system.

Suggestions: Adapt the method for isolation of various types of bacteria from various habitats. Bacteria capable of degrading pesticides, detergents, hydrocarbons and many types of organic matter have been isolated by going to a likely spot, gathering soil samples, placing in flasks, adding the selected material plus water and incubating from 1 week to many months at a suitable temperature.

Questions

1. Devise a quantitative method of determining the bacterial numbers capable of using a specific substrate.

2. What enrichment conditions would you suggest for isolation of chitin users? For users of a selected insecticide?

DATA SHEET

Acinetobacter Enrichment

Sample Number	Source	Bacterial counts Yeast extract	Acetate medium	Percent Acinetobacter	Description

Results and Discussion

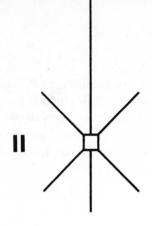

II   Ecological Succession

The ecological principle of succession refers to the orderly sequence of changes which take place in an ecosystem as it passes through developing stages toward maturity. Mature communities tend to increase in diversity, complexity, organization, order, ecological niches and to exhibit a greater efficiency of energy utilization; all of which contribute to greater stability in the ecosystem (Odum 1969). These changes require the expenditure of energy in order to satisfy the second law of thermodynamics.

Evolution and natural selection of individuals, communities or ecosystems are slow processes responding to gradual environmental changes. Rapid, extreme, environmental changes (volcanic eruption, floods, atomic bomb devastation) are responded to by successional regression or by new ecosystems composed of indigenous, opportunistic, immigrant or mutant organisms. No goal, purpose or direction is implied by any of these. It is sufficient to say that organisms inhabit the available space if they are biologically adapted to the growth conditions.

Consider two types of succession: (1) primary succession results when a system which consists of rock or soil containing no organic matter is invaded by organisms which are able to initiate a totally new regime; or (2) secondary succession results from allowing a field to revert to nature after having been cultivated. In either type of succession a number of factors will dictate which plants and animals are capable of becoming established. Organisms capable of dominating the habitat will then influence the subsequent successional pattern. Microorganisms will also be able to inhabit the ecosystem and they, too, will influence and be influenced by biotic and abiotic factors.

The exercises of this section of the manual will provide an ecosystem and offer methods for observing successional and population changes of the microecosystem in the laboratory. While this section contains the basic components for the study of microbial succession one may use many of the exercises from other sections to study specific functions during succession.

An important factor in succession is the opportunity for migration into the ecosystem. The dispersal of micro and macroorganisms may greatly alter the expected course of succession. Geographical barriers and other limiting factors may prevent adequate movement of organisms capable of competing in succession.

Succession may be either slow or rapid but successional stages usually demonstrate characteristics distinct from those of mature stages. Cooke et al. (1968) and Cooke (1967) have stressed these differences in their papers. An excellent discussion of ecological succession has been published and a list of the ecosystem attributes from that paper are reproduced below (Odum, 1969).

Aquatic microecosystems undergo a rapid succession which is similar in many ways to the ecological succession of natural habitats (Gorden et al. 1969; Hill and Gorden, unpublished). Similar events take place in lakes and ponds and in sewage—oxidation ponds. The natural process of eutrophication and succession of aquatic systems results in a gradual return to a terrestrial habitat over a long period of time. (See Section VI.) This successional time is shortened by man-induced eutrophication, however.

Odum's (1969) emphasis on the development of ecosystems points out the importance of successional stages. Brock (1967b) believes that an ecosystem should be described as an open system in a steady state. This definition implies that only mature systems which are exhibiting a P/R ratio near 1 are true ecosystems and that successional stages are not eligible for energy flow studies. Brock states that research dealing with succession are actually studies on the embryology of ecosystems. Brock's emphasis is on the thermodynamic relationships within the system; he raises a good point regarding this line of research. The feelings of this author are closely related to those of Odum. In fact, I believe that successional stages are more ecologically interesting than are mature ecosystems.

Table 1. A tabular model of ecological succession: trends to be expected in the development of ecosystems.

Ecosystem attributes	Developmental stages	Mature stages
Community energetics		
1. Gross production/community respiration (P/R ratio)	Greater or less than 1	Approaches 1
2. Gross production/standing crop biomass (P/B ratio)	High	Low
3. Biomass supported/unit energy flow (B/E ratio)	Low	High
4. Net community production (yield)	High	Low
5. Food chains	Linear, predominantly grazing	Weblike, predominantly detritus
Community structure		
6. Total organic matter	Small	Large
7. Inorganic nutrients	Extrabiotic	Intrabiotic
8. Species diversity—variety component	Low	High
9. Species diversity—equitability component	Low	High
10. Biochemical diversity	Low	High
11. Stratification and spatial heterogeneity (pattern diversity)	Poorly organized	Well-organized
Life history		
12. Niche specialization	Broad	Narrow
13. Size of organism	Small	Large
14. Life cycles	Short, simple	Long, complex
Nutrient cycling		
15. Mineral cycles	Open	Closed
16. Nutrient exchange rate, between organisms and environment	Rapid	Slow
17. Role of detritus in nutrient regeneration	Unimportant	Important
Selection pressure		
18. Growth form	For rapid growth ("r-selection")	For feedback control ("K-selection")
19. Production	Quantity	Quality
Overall homeostasis		
20. Internal symbiosis	Undeveloped	Developed
21. Nutrient conservation	Poor	Good
22. Stability (resistance to external perturbations)	Poor	Good
23. Entropy	High	Low
24. Information	Low	High

Reproduced from Odum, E. P. 1969. The strategy of ecosystem development. *Science* 164: 262-270, Table 1, p. 265.

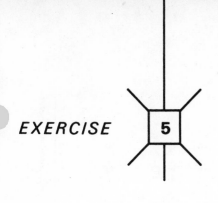

EXERCISE 5   THE USE OF MICROCOSMS

A microecosystem, a small model of a natural habitat, may be termed a microcosm. True, any attempt to enclose a natural habitat in an artificial container produces an artificial system. Experience has shown that aquatic microcosms are especially well suited for microbial ecological studies. It is felt the advantages of microcosms override the disadvantages for certain ecological studies. Beyers (1964) lists advantages of the microcosms as: (1) their discrete boundaries, (2) their small size, and (3) the fabrication of replicate ecosystems for experimental purposes. To these may be added (4) convenience of handling in the laboratory.

Microcosms may be developed in at least three ways: (1) components of the system may be randomly placed in a container, (2) selected components may be arranged in an order thought to be a suitable duplication of the ecosystem, or (3) components may be found in a container discarded in nature. Regardless of the mode of selection, the system should be allowed to stabilize over a period of time while under physical conditions which encourage an ecological succession toward maturity. Types of microcosms are limited only by the imagination of the investigator.

A specific aquatic microcosm for laboratory use was first isolated by Dr. R. Beyers from a sewage-oxidation pond. This community is self-supporting and can be replicated by the addition of 2.5 ml of the mature system into 125 ml of half strength Taub 36 media in 250 ml flasks. The system is capable of either heterotrophic or autotrophic succession dependent upon addition of either organic or inorganic materials when new systems are inoculated. Microorganisms are important components of the microcosm and the microheterotrophs fill numerous niches and contribute to the stability of the system. Studies of the heterotrophic succession have included measurements of productivity, bacterial and algal numbers, uptake of radioactive substrates and of the interactions between bacterial and algal populations (Gorden et al. 1969).

Table 2 provides evidence that this microcosm may be a suitable model of natural systems since it showed many of the attributes of ecosystems. Abbott (1966), Beyers (1963), and Cooke (1967) have demonstrated other values of microcosms for ecological studies. A detailed summary of aquatic microcosm research has been presented by Cooke (1969).

It is suggested that class members may wish to establish various types of microcosms in order to test certain ecological principles and methods described in this manual. Microcosms can be established readily from most aquatic systems. The author and his students have set up microecosystems capable of continuous support of invertebrates, algae and bacteria by simply filling containers with sea water or ephemeral lake water and placing them on a laboratory shelf in the sunlight. Unique microcosms may be developed from local polluted lakes and from hot springs (Allen & Brock 1968). A sample of microcosms under investigation in the laboratories of the author and of Dr. Robert J. Beyers is available upon request. Many of the exercises described in this manual have been used in microcosm studies.

PURPOSES

To illustrate the ease with which microcosms may be established. To provide a model system for use in the laboratory.

Table 2. A Comparison of Succession in the Microcosm with Trends to Be Expected in the Development of Ecosystems.

Ecosystem Attributes	Developmental Stages	Mature Stages	Microcosm	Day
Gross Production/Community Respiration (P/R Ratio)	< or > One	Approaches One	P/R < 1 P/R > 1 P/R ± 1	1–4 5–45 50–75
Gross Production/Standing Crop Biomass (P/B Ratio)	High	Low	P/B Low	45–75
Net Community Production (Yield)	High	Low	Peak Yield	20–35
Standing Crop Biomass And Organic Matter	Small	Large	Plateau 1.15 GM/1	50–75
Species Diversity	Low	High	Highest Lowest High	1 30 45–60
Stratification	Undeveloped	Well Developed	Increasing	24–75
Size of Organism	Small	Large	Increased with Age	1–75
Life Cycles	Short, Simple	Long, Complex	Simple Complex	1–60 60–1 yr.
Interdependence of Organisms	Low	High	High	1–75
Stability	Poor	Good	Improved with Age	1–75

Reproduced by permission of Gorden, R.W.; R.J. Beyers; E.P. Odum and R.G. Eagon, 1969. Studies of a simple laboratory microcosm: bacterial activities in a heterotrophic succession. *Ecology* 50: 86-100, Table 12, p. 99.

MATERIALS AND EQUIPMENT

Per group

100 ml graduated cylinder

5-10—250 ml flasks with cotton or cork stoppers

Pipets 1.0, 5.0 ml

Lighted growth chamber, window sill or other lighted growth area

Inoculum from established microcosm or water-mud sample from a nearby aquatic habitat

PROCEDURE

1. Make stock solutions of media according to the recipe provided here. Or, make up a suitable basal salts media according to whether you are developing a microcosm from the ocean, an estuary, an acid or alkaline ecosystem.

2. Combine appropriate amounts of the stock solution in a 2 liter flask. Bring to final 1 liter volume by adding 948 ml of distilled H_2O.

3. Add 0.05% proteose peptone or other substrate to one-half of the final solution. Label as heterotrophic (H) Taub.

4. Add 5.0 mg/liter thiamin and 35 mg/liter fixed nitrogen to the remaining solution. Label as autotrophic (A) Taub.

5. Dispense 125 ml of the solution (H and A in separate flasks) into 250 ml flasks. Label as H or A Taub.

6. Autoclave at 15 lbs. pressure, 120°C for 15-20 minutes, remove from autoclave and cool to incubating temperature.

7. Inoculate each flask with 2.5 to 5.0 ml of inoculum from an established microcosm or up to 10.0 ml of lake water. Flasks may be closed tightly or loosely cotton-stoppered.

8. Incubate under growth conditions similar to those which prevail in a natural habitat. In our laboratory standard growth conditions are 21°C ± 2°C, approximately 650-1000 ft. candles of light and a 12 hour dark-light cycle. Humidity in the chamber varies from 30-60%.

9. Heterotrophic (H) Taub provides a carbon source for the growth of bacteria and other heterotrophic organisms. Thus, the system first exhibits heterotrophic growth conditions—hence the name. Autotrophic growth conditions prevail in the no-carbon source flasks. The system is dependent upon the primary producers as a food source. Nitrate and the vitamin are added to stimulate the initial algal growth.

10. Due to different growth conditions the H and A flasks will support different population types and numbers. These systems can be compared by using exercises from this laboratory manual.

11. A wide variety of growth conditions may be used with the same microcosm. Our system has been exposed to such stress as 15-24 hours at 2°C and 1 day at 85°C with no visible effect on the total system. You may wish to first obtain basic data on your microcosm and then expose it to stress.

12. If the group wishes to observe successional stages at one time, it is easy to make up 10 flasks at one time and inoculate one each week.

13. Have fun with these microcosms and see how many different types you can find and develop.

Taub 36 Stock Solution

Solution no.	Salt(s)	g/L	1/2 Taub 36 ml/L of basic media for final concentration
	Basic media—Stock		
B	$MgSO_4 \cdot 7\,H_2O$	24.65	1
C	KH_2PO_4	13.60	1
	NaOH	3.20	
D	$CaCl_2 \cdot 2\,H_2O$	14.70	20
E	NaCl	5.84	30
F	$FeSO_4 \cdot 2\,H_2O$	24.90	0.125
	EDTA	26.10	
	NaOH	10.70	
G	H_3BO_4	1.854	0.5
	$ZnSO_4 \cdot 7\,H_2O$	0.287	
	$MnCl_2 \cdot 4\,H_2O$	1.98	
	$Na_2MoO_4 \cdot 5\,H_2O$	0.024	
	$CuSO_4 \cdot 5\,H_2O$	0.0499	
	$Co(NO_3)_2 \cdot 6\,H_2O$	0.291	

For Heterotrophic Media
   Add Bacto-peptone   0.5 g/L

For Autotrophic Media
   Add 35 mg/liter $NaNO_3$ Make up to 1 liter with
      5 mg/liter thiamin   distilled water

Name _____ Section _____ Date _____

DATA SHEET

The Use of Microcosms

| Microcosm | | Carbon source amount | Growth conditions Temperature °C | | light/Ftc. | | Bacterial populations | | |
Number	Age		day	night	on	off	Numbers	Dominant types	Percent chromagens

Results and Discussion

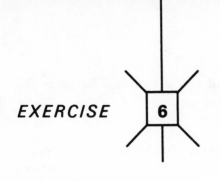

EXERCISE 6

COMMUNITY STRUCTURE AND PIGMENT RATIO

It has been noted that communities possess certain characteristics as they pass through developmental stages (Cooke et al. 1968). As a system approaches maturity; that is, as a dynamic equilibrium is established, the attributes of the ecosystem change as compared with the earlier successional stages (Table 1, p. 00). This table has been based on data taken from many ecological experiments. Although all the attributes postulated have never been tested on a single ecosystem a few were tested in a study of successional stages of a microcosm (Table 2, p. 00). Note especially that biochemical diversity is assumed to increase with maturity.

Margalef (1963a, 1963b) has suggested that an expression giving an indirect estimate of primary production on the basis of properties present in an ecosystem must include some term which reflects quantitatively the structure of the community. The pigment ratio D_{430}/D_{665} has been offered as a suitable indicator of community structure. A quantitative determination of the pigment chlorophyll a will be useful in estimating primary productivity of a system (aquatic or terrestrial). By determining the pigment ratio of the absorbancies at 430 mμ and 665 mμ a measure of community structure and an indication of the effect of nutrient depletion may be derived. McIntire (1968) has suggested that the ratio D_{480}/D_{665} is more appropriate since D_{480} has been the usual measurement for routine spectrophotometric determination of plant carotenoids.

Parsons and Strickland (1963) developed the first useful method of chlorophyll a determination. Several modifications have altered the method.

MATERIALS AND EQUIPMENT

Filtration equipment, including 0.45 μ filters
Centrifuge
Tissue grinder
Graduated centrifuge tubes
Spectrophotometric device
Acetone—90%
Mg^+CO_3

PROCEDURE

(For aquatic habitats—modify for terrestrial systems.)

1. A suitable sized sample is filtered on an HA or AA millipore filter, pore size 0.45 μ. The edges of the filter may be trimmed to remove as much nonplant material as possible.
2. Extract the chlorophyll by placing the filtered sample in 10 ml of 90% aqueous acetone for 24 hours in the dark.
   OR—place filter and sample in a tissue grinder, add 8 ml of 90% aqueous acetone plus Mg^+ carbonate for stability. Grind the sample carefully for 2 minutes or until the filter and sample are completely homogenized.
3. Pour ground sample into a graduated centrifuge tube, rinse mortar and pestle with sufficient 90% aqueous acetone to bring the volume to 10 ml.
4. Centrifuge for 10-15 minutes at 2500 rpm to bring nonchlorophyll material out of solution. Chlorophyll remains in solution.

33

5. Decant to spectrophotometer tube and read at 665 mμ and 430 mμ using a Beckman DU spectrophotometer, a Spectronic 20 or other suitable measuring device.
6. The reading at 665 mμ provides a measurement of Chlorophyll a.

Recent efforts to improve the accuracy of the method of Parsons and Strickland have been made. Moss (1967a) has advanced a rather complicated method for estimating the relationship between chlorophyll a and pheophytin a as a 430:410 mμ ratio. He also has presented a method (1967b) for an estimation of the quantity of chlorophyll a in fresh water.

A much simpler method has been offered by Lorenzen (1967) and is presented here.

A Method for Accurate Determination of Chlorophyll a

PROCEDURE

1. Filter 10 ml of water containing a small quantity of $MgCO_3$ through a Whatman GF/C glass paper filter or suitable substitute of 0.45 μ pore size.
2. Filter the sample to be analyzed through the filter.
3. Grind the filter in 5.0 ml of 90% acetone until thoroughly macerated.
4. Pour ground sample to graduated centrifuge tube.
5. Rinse mortar and pestle with sufficient acetone to bring solution to 10 ml plus filter.
6. Allow 30-60 minutes for pigments to elute.
7. Centrifuge at 2500-3000 $\times$ g.
8. Decant to spectrophometer tubes.
9. Read at 750 and 665 mμ in a spectrophotometer.
10. Add 2 drops of 1 N HCl and read again at 750 and 665 mμ.
11. Correct absorbance by subtracting reading difference between the 750 and the 665 mμ readings.
12. Enter the readings obtained at 665 mμ corrected for 750 mμ reading, in the following equations:

$$\text{Chlorophyll } a \text{ (mg/m}^3) = \frac{A \times K \times (665_0 - 665_a) \times v}{V_f \times 1}$$

$$\text{Pheophytin } a \text{ (mg/m}^3) = \frac{A \times K \times (R\ 665_a - 665_0) \times v}{V_f \times 1}$$

where:

   A = absorption coefficient of chlorophyll a
   A = 11.0
   K = factor to equate the reduction in absorbancy to initial chlorophyll concentration, 1.7:0.7, or 2.43
   665_0 = absorbance before acidification
   665_a = absorbance after acidification
   v = volume of acetone used for extraction (ml)
   V_f = liters of water filtered
   1 = path length of cuvette (cm)
   R = maximum ratio of 665_0:665_a in the absence of pheo-pigments, 1.7

Thus, the concentration of chlorophyll a has been corrected for that degraded to pheophytin.

Questions

1. What are the biochemical reactions which result in the degradation of chlorophyll a?
2. At what wavelengths are the peaks of the different chlorophylls most pronounced? the carotenoids?
3. What are other problems and causes of interference in chlorophyll determinations?
4. Design experiments in which chlorophyll content of an ecosystem may be shown to be related to: (a) primary production, (b) living biomass, (c) uptake of $^{14}CO_2$, (d) successional stage, or (e) other ecosystem attributes.

DATA SHEET

Chlorophyll Determination

Sample number	Spectrophometric readings — mμ						Chlorophyll mg/m^3
	430	480	665a	665b	750a	750b	

CHLOROPHYLL DETERMINATION

Results and Discussion

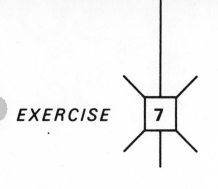

EXERCISE 7   **DOMINANT BACTERIAL TYPES**

Bacterial populations of many habitats undergo relatively short generation times and have rapid turnover rates. The populations are constantly changing in numbers and dominant types. Using direct microscopic observations bacterial successions may go unobserved due to the similar morphological appearance of many organisms. Viable counts of dilution plates reveal more than just the minimum number of cells/ml. By carefully observing and counting the different colony types, the ecologically successful microorganisms will be indicated within the limits of the growth conditions.

MATERIALS AND EQUIPMENT

Same as in Exercises 1 and 2.
Use dilution plates from previous exercises.

PROCEDURE

1. After making the dilution, pour or streak plates (Exercise 1 and previous experience); allow the colonies to grow for 8-12 days at habitat temperature, in the light, if possible.
2. Examine the plates under a stereo microscope using sufficient magnification to view colony morphology. Although it is true that many bacterial colonies have similar morphology, much variety in surface and subsurface colony structure may be noted.
3. **Caution:** (a) observe lower dilutions to note colony types not present on the plates containing "significant numbers"; (b) compare plate counts with direct counts since sporeformers and other bacteria may be present in high numbers on agar plates, although they are relatively inactive in the system; and (c) note that viable numbers may not be a correct indication of the ecological importance of microorganisms in the system.
4. Algal colonies growing in the agar may be counted and compared with direct counts.
5. It may be necessary to isolate the various bacterial types; culture them axenically; make dilution pour plates of the pure cultures and observe both surface and submerged colonies in order to recognize them on the mixed culture dilution plates.

Questions

1. What types of bacteria and algae which were seen under direct observation were not observed on dilution plates? How can you be certain that the bacteria have the same morphology on the media as in the natural habitat?
2. **Suggestions:** Sample various habitats and compare cell types. Where are the bacteria most abundant—in the mud-water interface, attached to leaves and stems or in the water surface film?
3. How often must samples be taken to obtain an accurate estimate of population growth?
4. Can accurate estimates of populations be made by sampling in the same place daily or weekly? in a pond? in a large lake or ocean? in a microcosm?

DATA SHEET

Dominant Bacterial Types

Type of system	Dilution	Bacterial types	Total count	Algal colonies	Observations and comments

DOMINANT BACTERIAL TYPES

Results and Discussion

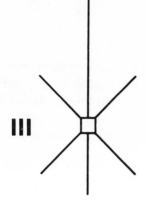

III   Ecological Functions of Microorganisms

Many factors have deterred microbiologists from ecological studies. Two of these factors are the difficulty of determining and measuring specific functions of microorganisms in natural habitats. Function is commonly used to indicate the general role of organisms in the environment. For example the term "decomposer" is used to indicate organisms whose main activity appears to be the degradation of large organic particles. "Function" is a nebulous term when applied to populations in an ecosystem. The critical use of the term "ecological function" may lead to a clarification of one or more specific activities of a species in the system. The function may then be measured and a rate determined.

In the laboratory, axenic microbial cultures may be shown to function in a specific way or in a variety of ways dependent upon the substrate and environmental stress applied. Extrapolation of laboratory results to nature are unrealistic unless similar environmental conditions pertain. However, laboratory studies may reveal the probable activities of organisms in nature, if not the magnitude of these activities.

The exercises of Section IV contain methods used by investigators when they wish to determine (1) the rate of an activity within an ecosystem, (2) which microorganisms are participating in that activity and/or (3) what the function of certain microorganisms may be in a particular habitat. Another purpose of this section is to explain a few ecological uses for radioactive compounds. The user may modify these methods for future use in specific research situations.

Nutrient recycling is one of the important functions of microorganisms in nature. The fate of higher plants and animals is dependent upon the recycling of phosphate, nitrogen, sulfur and carbon in the system. Other elements must also be released during the processes of decomposition. Action which results in the tie-up or long-range binding of nutrients, making them inaccessible for use by living organisms, may serve as an inhibitor to the system and may be a cause of limiting the productivity of the system.

Nutrient cycling studies of a forested watershed in New England (Hubbard Brook) have shown that many essential elements are cycled in a manner which is not totally dependent upon microorganisms (Likens et al. 1967). These workers have described an ecosystem where the losses of calcium, magnesium, sodium and chloride have exceeded the input while potassium showed a slight increase during the study period. They conclude: "Assuming that the biota and soils of the ecosystem are near dynamic equilibrium, these losses are counterbalanced by chemical decomposition of the underlying bedrock and till."

Subsequently, a portion of the same watershed was "clearcut" with the downed trees trimmed in order that the vegetation was no more than 1.5 m above ground. A comparative study revealed a loss of NO_3^- from the system in large amounts; that is, 5.70 kg/hectare. This nutrient loss was attributed to increased activity of the soil microorganisms, including the decomposers and nitrifying types, which led to an increase of dissolved nitrate in leaching waters. The increase of NO_3^- in runoff streams exceeded established pollution levels of 10 ppm for more than 1 year, and algal blooms appeared during the summer.

Nutrient cycling and turnover times of essential materials are of ultimate importance in every type of ecosystem. The significance of this type of study is emphasized when one realizes the number of acres which are clearcut of forest or crops during a year in the United States. The carbon, nitrogen and sulfur cycles have been emphasized in microbiology texts. Often a system may be limited due to a deficiency of one or more of these three minerals. Commonly longterm tie-up of carbon, nitrogen, or sulfur affects primary producers first and then the consumers. Other elements, although required in smaller amounts, may be of equal importance.

The importance of microorganisms in the release of important nutrients has resulted in an overemphasis of the decomposer role of bacteria, fungi and actinomycetales. (See Section VI.) Nutrient cycling may be easily illustrated by enclosing an ecosystem in a tightly-capped container and exposing it to constant or intermittent light. With only the influx of light energy the system may reach an equilibrium in which biomass is limited by the availability of an essential element. By addition of this element to the system one may increase the production of the system to another plateau level—limited by the same or another essential component.

Alternately, one may change the system so that the limiting material is more rapidly cycled. Thus, the productivity of the system may be enhanced by a rapid uptake and release of the limiting material. In nature, a system may be limited by lack of various nutrients; this is one reason why domestic crops are fertilized. However, the recycling of essential materials may depend upon the presence of microorganisms and macroorganisms.

The decomposer trophic level rightfully includes invertebrates and vertebrates which ingest and egest detritus, adding to it organic acids and other components. Reingestion of feces is practiced by certain mammals and invertebrates, thus speeding the decomposition. Evidence is available that certain invertebrates reingest their feces and assimilate the bacteria which are growing in the waste material. Javornicky and Prokesova (1963) believe that protozoa are effective in maintaining bacterial populations in the log phase, thereby increasing bacterial effectiveness as decomposers. A review of this topic (Guady and Gaudy 1966) reveals that protozoan activity may be unnecessary.

Do not restrict bacteria, fungi, and other microorganisms to the decomposer trophic level. Remember that they contribute in other ways to nutrient recycling; i.e., nitrogen fixation, denitrification, photosynthesis, chemoautotrophic activities, etc.

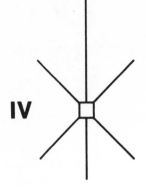

The Use of Radioactive Substrates in Microbial Ecology

IV

Compounds containing radioactive isotopes which can be assimilated by living organisms in a natural habitat offer diverse opportunities for ecological study. Both organic and inorganic compounds have been proven useful in metabolic and ecological investigations. By using inorganic radioactive isotopes it is possible to trace the movement of certain minerals through the food web of a community. Also, the amounts of materials assimilated may be compared with the amounts which are lost as excretions and feces. Rates of nutrient cycling in various ecosystems have been estimated in this manner.

Radioactive organic compounds may be specifically labeled for metabolic studies. Thus, a glucose molecule labeled with ^{14}C on the 1 carbon (^{14}C-1-Glucose) would yield different metabolic information than that gained by investigations using ^{14}C-6-Glucose or ^{14}C-U-Glucose; the latter compound having all carbons labeled equally. The variety of compounds and investigations possible is vast. Carbon dioxide, acetate, glucose and other simple carbon compounds have been used in ecological work. Inorganic labeled compounds used include ^{3}H — thymidine, ^{32}P, ^{137}Cs, ^{45}Ca, ^{35}S, ^{62}Zn and ^{42}K.

Numerous problems arise in the interpretation of data derived from studies involving radioisotopes. Isotopes may be adsorbed by cells, detritus, or by inorganic compounds. Certain cells may preferentially exclude or take up radioisotopes due to weight variations and for unknown reasons. Other cells and organisms may accumulate and store relatively large amounts of radioisotopes. Organic compounds may be assimilated in their entirety or a high percentage of the substrate may be lost as $^{14}CO_2$. Carbon dioxide may be quickly utilized by both autotrophic and heterotrophic organisms. In heterotrophs, 12 to 14 or more pathways of CO_2 assimilation have been described (Wood and Stjernholm 1962). Sorokin (1965) has estimated that in 3-5% of the assimilated carbon of common heterotrophs and 30-90% of the carbon of certain other bacteria was incorporated CO_2.

Users of radioactive substrates must use extreme caution in the use of these compounds. Observe safety measures advised by local, state and national agencies regarding the use and disposal of radioactive materials.

The purpose of this section is to explain a few ecological uses of radioactive compounds. The user may modify these methods for future experiments.

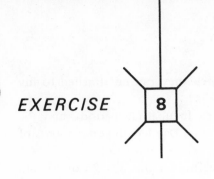

EXERCISE 8

THE USE OF CARBON-14 IN THE MEASUREMENT OF PRIMARY PRODUCTIVITY IN AQUATIC HABITATS

PURPOSES

To measure phytoplankton photosynthetic rates in aquatic systems.

To illustrate some problems involved in measurements of primary productivity.

Much of the emphasis on microbial ecology in recent years has centered on aquatic systems. Interactions between bacteria and phytoplankton have been studied, and methods of primary productivity measurement are necessary tools for the microbial ecologist. We must be aware of factors which affect photosynthesis as well as the rates of photosynthesis in natural systems.

A standardized method for such measurements has been suggested by Goldman (1963) and serves as the basis for this exercise.

MATERIALS AND EQUIPMENT

0.45 μ membrane filters—47 mm or 25 mm diameter; filtering equipment

Vacuum pump

Pipets—5.0 ml and 1.0 ml sizes

Sampling bottles—nonmetallic

Screw cap tubes

Automatic hypodermic syringe, 5.0 ml size

100 ml hypodermic syringe

125 ml ground glass-stoppered bottles—light and dark

Metered chains or line

Counting device—Liquid Scintillation counter or G.M. ultra thin window-gas flow counter

Radioactive isotope $Na_2{}^{14}CO_3$, approximately 50-100 microcuries

PROCEDURE

1. Using de-ionized, glass distilled H_2O, make $Na_2{}^{14}CO_3$ solutions, activity range 2-5 $\mu c/ml$, in sufficient quantities to last for the entire study. Mix with an 0.1 N NaOH solution using a glass covered magnetic stirring bar; mix well to prevent a pH gradient. Adjust to pH less than 9.5.

2. Samples should be taken immediately prior to incubation. Nonmetallic sampling containers are preferred since metallic containers stimulate CO_2 fixation or inhibit photosynthesis (Goldman 1963). Depending on the depth of the photic zone and the size of the body of water, samples may be secured which will be representative of the entire area or of a localized habitat.

3. Transfer samples immediately to incubation bottles or tubes, cap and store in a dark, insulated container.

4. The carbon —14 solution may be pipetted aseptically from the sterile stock to the incubation bottle or tube after the water sample has been taken. A final concentration equal to 2-5 microcuries/125 ml of sample is suggested. Goldman (1963) has described a rapid method of adding 1 ml quantities of solution to a large number of incubation bottles using a 100 ml hypodermic syringe. Such a method may be unnecessary for a class experiment but extremely valuable for field research.

5. Heterotrophic microorganisms may also assimilate $^{14}CO_2$; as a measure of dark $^{14}CO_2$ fixation, both light and dark incubation containers should be used. Dark bottles are readily constructed by wrapping with black tape or layers of aluminum foil and testing for leaks.

47

Incubation containers should have a ring at the neck by which they can be attached to the hooks at measured intervals on the line.

6. Submerge the bottles to the desired depth and incubate. Incubation periods may be determined empirically and may vary from 20 minutes to 6 hours. Day length and amounts of solar radiation affect the accuracy of photosynthetic estimates.

7. At the conclusion of the incubation period samples may be filtered through 25 or 47 mm diameter, 0.45 μ pore size membrane filters at 15 inches Hg vacuum. Rinse with 5 ml of 3% formalin. (10% formalin may be added to the incubated sample and stored indefinitely.) Rinse with .003 N HCl only if inorganic precipitation is indicated.

8. The concentration of biomass of the system dictates the amount to be filtered and the diameter of the filter used. The author has routinely used 25 mm diameter filters while filtering 0.1 ml to 5.0 ml samples from microcosms. This size fits the bottom of liquid scintillation vials. Lind and Campbell (1969) suggest the use of a 47 mm diameter millipore filter for filtering larger volumes. They place the filter, coiled slightly with the algae on the inside, in a similar 20 ml vial. Planchets are available into which either size filter will fit.

Counting

Liquid scintillation counter. Add 15-20 ml of scintillation solution, i.e., 0.4% PPO (2,5-diphenyl-oxazole) and 0.01% dimethyl POPOP 1, 4-bis-2-(4 methyl-5-phenyloxazole)-benzene (or a comparable commercial solution) in reagent grade toluene to each vial. Recap tightly and store in the dark.

Gas flow planchet counters. Dried filters may be glued in place, algae side up. Counting may require an extended period of time; 2000-5000 disintegrations should be registered. Each counter used should be standardized against a known algal standard. (It may be advisable to dissolve the sample into the toluene cocktail for more accurate counting. This may be accomplished by the use of commercial solubilizers.) After counting with the Gieger-Mueller unit, Goldman (1963) suggests that the sample be converted to CO_2 and its absolute activity determined by gas phase or scintillation methods.

Questions

1. What are the differences of productivity expected (and found) at various levels of the system?
2. How do you account for the differences? Might the bacterial populations vary with depth or for other reasons and thereby influence photosynthesis rates?
3. Will the difference between dark and light bottles, (light minus dark fixation) compensate for the effect bacteria have on the system?
4. What contributions do microheterotrophs make to the photosynthetic process in nature?

DATA SHEET

Primary Productivity

Radioactive substrate data

Batch/Lot no. _____
Specific Activity _____
Concentration/100 ml _____
Type of counter used _____
Model no. _____
Counting efficiency _____

Type of system _____
Name of system _____
Physical-chemical data
pH _____ Temp. _____
0_2 _____ Depth _____
$C0_2$ _____ Time _____
Secchi
reading _____

Vial number	Sample description	CPM			DPM corrected	Primary productivity mgC/m³ /hour
		1	2	3		

PRIMARY PRODUCTIVITY

Results and Discussion

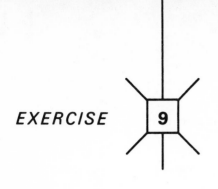

MEASUREMENT OF "HETEROTROPHIC POTENTIAL" OF AQUATIC BACTERIA USING RADIOACTIVE SUBSTRATES

The rate of uptake of ^{14}C compounds was suggested by Parsons and Strickland (1961) as an indication of heterotrophic activity in aquatic systems. They were able to determine the heterotrophic uptake of C using the formula:

$$mg\ C/m^3\ /hr = \frac{c.f.\ (S + A)}{C\ u\ t}$$

where:

u = μC of ^{14}C added
A = added concentration of substrate Carbon
S = concentration of the endogeneous substrate
t = time in hours of incubation
c = cpm of filtered organisms
C = cpm of 1.0 μC of ^{14}C discrimination

These workers showed that the uptake of acetate and the presence of glucose were independent factors because even the addition of 10 times as much glucose as acetate did not affect the uptake rate of acetate.

Recently several investigators have developed methods for determining the capacity of bacterial populations to use specific organic compounds in nature. The stated purposes of these experiments are (1) to measure the heterotrophic potential of the microorganisms, and (2) to measure the heterotrophic activity at a given time. The substrates most frequently used are glucose and acetate due to their ready incorporation into metabolic pathways. Wright and Hobbie (1966) believe that uptake of labeled glucose and acetate by natural populations may follow Michaelis-Menten kinetic rules. Vaccaro and Jannasch (1966) suggest, however, that apparent kinetic uptake by mixed populations is due to the activity of a single dominant species or more than one species with similar capacities to utilize and compete for the labeled substrate.

The uptake of radioactive substrates as a method of measurement of autotrophic and heterotrophic activity of microorganisms in natural habitats requires extreme care in application and interpretation. Suitable methods have been devised for the measurement of photosynthesis and productivity of a community (Goldman 1963). Various suggestions have been made for the measurement of bacterial activity in aquatic systems (Gorden et al. 1969; Wright and Hobbie 1966; Parsons and Strickland 1961). Gray et al. (1965) have developed methods for measuring the rate of production of fatty acids in the rumen of sheep. Their method may be modified to make other observations concerning microbial activity in the rumen. Odum and Kuenzler (1963) have shown that radioactive substances injected into or taken into the vascular plant system can be traced to primary and secondary consumers (mainly arthropods) and a food web may be determined.

The methods of Odum and Kuenzler (1963) offer distinct possibilities for microbial ecology. Little is known concerning the loss of energy from vascular plants to microorganisms although an extrapolation of literature data indicates that 5-7% of the gross production may pass to microorganisms prior to harvest (Gorden 1969). One might label a plant, enclose it in a fine mesh chamber to prevent losses to insects and then determine losses of substrate taken up by bacteria feeding on excretions present on the leaves and roots. Radioautographic techniques are useful for such determinations. (Note Exercise 11.)

OBJECTIVE

To determine the heterotrophic activity of a system by measurement of the assimilation of a radioactive carbon source.

MATERIALS AND EQUIPMENT

As listed in Exercise 8

Radioactive substrates of choice; suggested substrates include ^{14}C-U-Glucose, ^{14}C-U-Acetate.

PROCEDURE

1. Radioactive substrates may be mixed in distilled water, buffer solutions, filtered pond water or a known basal salts solution.
2. Mix radioactive substrates in batch lots so that a concentration of 2-5 microcuries/ml will be available for the entire study. These solutions should be filtered, sterilized, and stored in sterile condition at 4°C.
3. Calculate the amount of substrate available per ml; it may be necessary to add a known amount of unlabeled substrate to the solution so that endogenous substrate in the natural system will not affect the rate of uptake of the radioactive substrate. Endogenous acetate and glucose concentrations may range from 0-10 μg/liter in natural systems (Wright and Hobbie 1966). Bioassay procedures for natural waters have been outlined by Allen (1968) and Hobbie and Wright (1965).
4. Use water samples obtained aseptically as in Exercise 8. Take precautions in order that bacteria from hands and equipment do not enter the sample.
5. Add 100 ml of sample to a 125 ml glass-stoppered bottle. Add 1.0 ml of isotope solution to the bottle. Shake and incubate by suspending in the habitat or incubate in a growth chamber at comparable temperature and light intensity. Light and dark bottles should be incubated.
6. Incubation periods may range from 1 hour to 6 hours. (The author finds little difference between incubation periods of 20 minutes and 1 hour in his microcosm experiments.) Select incubation conditions which seem appropriate for the system.
7. Control bottles containing samples inactivated by autoclaving, steaming, addition of 10% formalin or by some other means may be incubated in the presence of the isotope. In this manner the isotope adsorbed by cells and not assimilated may be detected.
8. After incubation inactivation of the sample, filtration and counting procedures should follow those of Exercise 8.
9. Determine differences between dark and light bottles. Extrapolate from sample to units of area as m^2 and m^3. Express results as approximate net photosynthesis in mg C/m^2/hour and as mg C/m^3/hour.
10. Total CO_2 content of the water should be estimated. Although gravimetric methods described by Goldman appear best, there is presently no standardized, accurate, field method available.

In order to relate initial primary productivity measurements to volume and area units one must consider both the volume of sample and unit volume. As an example, assume that the amount of sample filtered was 100 ml and that the assimilated substrate equaled 2.4 mg C fixed/liter of sample. This amount may first be corrected for a 6% isotope effect; $2.4 \times 1.06 = 2.54$ mgC per liter. To determine production/m^3/hr:

$$2.54 \text{ mg C/liter} \times 10^3 \text{ liter} = mgC/m^3$$

To determine production/m^3/day:

$$2.54 \times 10^3 \text{ mgC hours of daylight} = mgC/m^3/day$$

DATA SHEET

Heterotrophic Activity

Sample Number	Description	CPM 1	2	3	Mean	mgC/m^3/hour

Results and Discussion

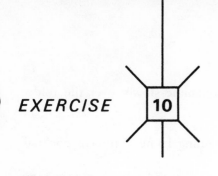

EXERCISE 10

CAPTURE OF CO₂ RESPIRED BY HETEROTROPHS IN AQUATIC SYSTEMS

Early methods of measuring the uptake of ^{14}C-substrates by heterotrophic and photosynthetic organisms failed to account for the respired $^{14}CO_2$. Hobbie and Crawford (1969) have developed a suitable method for measuring the amount of $^{14}CO_2$ lost by respiration. Their work serves as a basis for this exercise.

If one adds ^{14}C-U-Glucose, acetate or other ^{14}C labeled substrate to a system (as described in Exercises 8 and 9) a portion of the carbon will be respired. No investigator has determined how many times this $^{14}CO_2$ may be reassimilated by the same population or by members of another population during the incubation period. One may imagine a rather complex movement of the CO_2 through an ecosystem, however. Wouldn't it be fascinating to be able to watch organic and inorganic molecules pass from organism to organism in the system? We cannot do that and must ask one of you ingenious young people to develop a suitable method. Until then we must use a procedure similar to the one described here. This technique simply captures the $^{14}CO_2$ respired and adsorbed onto filter paper soaked in phenethylamine.

In Exercises 8 and 9 the $^{14}CO_2$ respired is lost from the incubation vessel as the lid is removed. In this exericse the $^{14}CO_2$ is not allowed to escape from the closed system. This procedure may serve as a control procedure for Exercises 8 and 9.

MATERIALS AND EQUIPMENT

Per group:

    5-25 ml Erlenmeyer flasks or bottles
    Rubber septum stoppers for each flask
    Plastic cups
    Wire
    Whatman no. 1 Chromatographic paper
    $2 NH_2 SO_4$
    Phenethylamine
    Scintillation vials—PPO and POPOP Scintillation cocktail
    Toluene—^{14}C as an internal standard

PROCEDURE

1. Fasten a plastic cup to the wire and suspend it from the rubber septum.
2. Cut and accordian-fold a 25 × 51 mm piece of Whatman No. 1 paper. Insert this into the cup.
3. Add 5.0 ml of water sample to the flask.
4. Pipet in 1 μC of ^{14}C-U-Glucose or other carbon substrate.
5. Cap and incubate under habitat conditions. Flask should look similar to Figure 10-1.
6. After incubation for 2-4 hours inject 0.2 ml of $2NH_2SO_4$ solution via hypodermic needle through the septum into the water sample. Withdraw needle. This solution should kill the sample and release the CO_2 from the water.

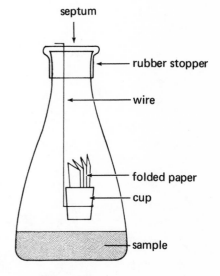

Figure 10-1.

55

7. Using another hypodermic needle inject 0.2 ml of phenethylamine slowly over the folded paper. Withdraw needle.
8. Shake the flask at room temperature for 1 hour.
9. Remove the folded paper and place in scintillation vials containing 15 ml of toluene cocktail.
10. Count on the liquid scintillation counter.
11. Filter the sample using 0.45 μ filters, rinse with 10 ml of H_2O, dry and count using the same procedure.
12. Following counting add a known amount of internal standard (Toluene$-^{14}$ C); i.e., 0.1 μC to each of the vials.
13. Recount the filter and paper.
14. After recount determine the efficiency of the machine and estimate the percent of the radioactivity on the filter and paper which was counted.
15. Compute the amount of $^{14}CO_2$ released due to respiration of the microorganisms.
16. Hobbie and Crawford's (1969) data indicate that the amount of $^{14}CO_2$ respired varies with the type of substrate used. Approximately 61% of the aspartic acid was given off and only 30% of the glucose-6 was respired. How do your results compare with theirs?

Questions

1. Explain why a large percentage of aspartic acid was respired. What metabolic pathway was in use?
2. Where would glucose-6 be incorporated into cellular material? Why was 30% respired?
3. What efficiency of assimilation would one normally expect for a simple compound such as those used?
4. Devise other experiments which would clarify the respiration of large amounts of $^{14}CO_2$ from different radioactive carbon substrates.
5. Do you think that shorter incubation times would affect the $^{14}CO_2$ amounts respired? Why?

DATA SHEET

CO₂ Capture

Sample Number	Substrate	CPM 0.45 μ Paper	Filter	CPM Toluene ¹⁴C Paper	Filter	Percent CO₂ respired

Results and Discussion

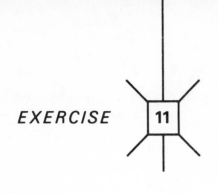

EXERCISE 11   AUTORADIOGRAPHIC METHODS

Autoradiography is based on the reaction of radioactive substances with photographic film or emulsion. This reaction, an exposure similar to that of light photography, must therefore take place in the dark. The radioactive substrate, when exposed to the film or emulsion, will take its own picture. In this manner bacteria which have taken up radioactive substances may be located in a natural system. Brock and Brock (1966, 1968) have demonstrated the value of this method as applied to ecology. This exercise is based on the method developed in their laboratory at Indiana University.

The type of film or emulsion used depends upon the system being studied. One may use a large sheet of film to find the distribution of an isotope in the leaf of a plant or a microscope slide dipped in emulsion for isotopic uptake by bacteria. The choice of label also is important: (1) the labeled substrate must be assimilated and retained by the organism under study, (2) this label must not be selected against in nature, and (3) the radiation from the isotope should not spread out from the labeled object. Tritium (^{3}H) is an isotope which gives a clear, well-defined pattern on film or emulsion whereas ^{32}P spreads out indiscriminately. ^{14}C is a common and suitable isotope for many experiments.

MATERIALS AND EQUIPMENT

Emulsion—NTB-2 or NTB-3 Kodak
Developer Kodak D19
Fixer Kodak Acid Fixer
Isotopes—Radioactive substrates
Screwcapped test tubes
Microscope slides
Ulrich's adhesive
Bakelite slide box
Light tight box
Cytological slide rack
Plastic 1 qt. freezer containers—3-6
A light-tight darkroom is essential
Wratten No. 2 red safelight, 25 watt bulb
Two timers without luminescent dials
Pasteur pipettes
Water bath, inner pan, holder
Neoprene rubber coated test tube rack
Formalin, 10%
Coplin slide jars

PROCEDURE

1. Expose the sample to radioactive isotopes under appropriate conditions as described in Exercises 8 and 9, kill using 10% formalin, store until needed.
2. Clean microscope slides by using alcohol, potassium dichromate solution or Bon Ami (do not use detergent).
3. Spread Ulrich's adhesive lightly on one side of the clean slide with finger or brush.
   Ulrich's adhesive:
      1 ml concentrated ammonia, 1 ml Na silicate, 100 ml distilled H_2O, mix thoroughly.

4. Add one drop of the labeled sample to the slide using a pasteur pipette, spread out and examine cell concentration using phase microscope, if available. Adjust concentration so that the mixture is thin enough to see through.

5. Wash 3 times in distilled H_2O in Coplin jars to remove debris and formalin. Wash by dipping in jar 1 minute each, change water in jars every 4-5 slides. Allow slides to dry while lying flat.

Emulsion Dipping: *Emulsion must never be exposed to light.* To do so exposes the emulsion and renders it useless. Expose emulsion to Wratten no. 2 safelight only.

1. All handling of emulsion, dipping, racking of slides, etc. must be done in the dark. The location of all materials, equipment, and the procedure should be clearly in mind prior to turning off the light; note Figure 11-1. All emulsion must be cleaned from glassware, equipment table, sink, in darkroom prior to leaving. During steps 2-5 use the safelight only.

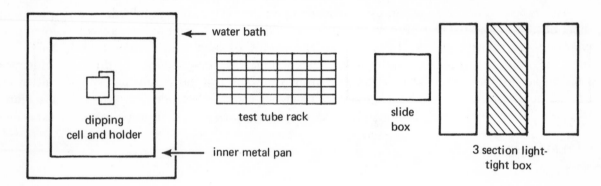

Figure 11-1.

2. In the *Dark,* warm the stock bottle of emulsion to 45°C. Pour 12 ml into a small vial, well marked at the 12 ml level. Fill a vial with 18 ml of distilled water. When ready to dip slides, pour the emulsion and water together into a beaker, stir with a glass rod without making bubbles. Warm diluted emulsion to 45°C. Pour from beaker to suitable dipping container held in water bath by holder on ring stand. Inner pan should fit into water bath and catch any emulsion accidentally dropped so that the water bath is not contaminated for later use. Emulsion in dipping cell should be deep enough to dip slide nearly to frosted portion.

3. While dipping, hold slide vertically, immerse slide to bottom of dipping cell. Withdraw slide smoothly and slowly. Place in latex-covered, test tube rack so that slide edges only touch rack sides. Have frosted side of the slides in consistent direction for easier handling and placing in slide rack later. Allow to dry for 30-45 minutes.

4. Place dry slides in the slide box. Make two lists of the slides, add 1 copy of the list to the top of the slide box. Place the slide box inside the light-tight box. Tape the second copy of the list to the top of the light-tight box. Seal with rubber band or tape around outer box to prevent accidental exposure of slides.

5. Check darkroom carefully. Make certain all materials such as emulsion, both diluted and concentrated, are stored in the dark; then the light may be turned on. Clean up area carefully, washing emulsion from all materials.

Exposure of Slides

The exposure period may vary with the amount of radioactive substrate taken up by the members of the system. This time period will depend upon the specific activity of the radioactive material and with the type of isotope being used. By making duplicate slides one may develop the first set after 2 to

4 days and the second set may be developed as dictated by the condition of the first. Every set of slides should contain 1 or 2 control slides which will indicate the degree of background radiation of the emulsion.

Developing

Developer and fixer are standard products. Filter through medium filter paper and store in gallon containers in the darkroom. Both may be exposed to light. All developing must be carried out in the dark as follows:

1. Depending on the number of slides to be developed have 1 or 2 sets of plastic boxes containing developer, distilled water and fixer as seen in Figure 11-2. Have sufficient liquid in each to cover slides.

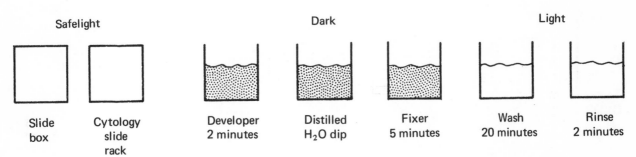

Figure 11-2.

2. Have timers, containers, slides, and racks in most effective setup for the darkroom being used.
3. With safelight on, transfer slides from light-tight box to cytology slide rack. Be careful not to scratch slides.
4. Set timer for 2 minutes. *Turn safelight OFF.*
5. With safelight *OFF,* place slides in developer and remove after two minutes.
6. Dip in distilled water briefly.
7. Place slides in fixer for 5 minutes.
8. Remainder of procedure may take place in complete light or under the safelight. Wash for 20 minutes in running water and, finally, rinse for two (2) minutes in distilled water.
9. Allow slides to dry in clean slide rack, test tube rack or box and then view under the microscope.

Interpretation of autoradiographic slides depends upon the material being studied and the purpose of the investigation. Brock (1967a, 1967b) has been able to determine the growth rate of the large marine bacterium, *Leucothrix,* and to study the mode of growth. Quantitative assessment of the uptake of the isotope may be possible by counting the exposed individual silver grains. This method is quite laborious but may be worth the effort in some instances.

An important use of the autoradiographic method is to determine which microorganisms assimilated the radioactive substrate. The silver grains of the film or emulsion become black when exposed to the radioactivity. These darkened grains will contrast with the cells and the types of cells which have radioactivity can be readily determined. Photographs may be made of the slide, under oil immersion magnification, using Polaroid film or standard film in color or black and white.

Valuable references on micro-autoradiographic techniques have been prepared by Brock and Brock (1968) and Rogers (1967).

Questions

1. What modifications of the autoradiographic procedure do you suggest?
2. In what way might this method be used to estimate the quantity of assimilated radioactive substrate?
3. Suggest ecological applications of this technique.
4. Using this method devise an experiment which will indicate function and rate of function of a specific microbial population in a natural habitat.

DATA SHEET

Autoradiographic Methods

Sample number	Slide number	Exposure time	Silver grains/cell	Description and drawing

Results and Discussion

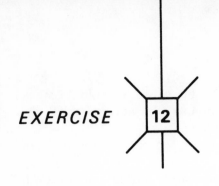

EXERCISE 12

TRACER TECHNIQUES IN NUTRIENT CYCLING

Whereas radioactive organic compounds may be assimilated, excreted and respired in complex systems, their uses as tracers are commonly limited to short-term experiments. Inorganic nutrient cycling studies are of great interest to microbial ecologists. There are advantages in the use of ^{54}Mn, ^{65}Zn, ^{137}Cs, ^{45}Ca, and ^{85}Sr in ecosystem studies. More than one isotope may be added to the system at one time; the half-life of each allows sufficient radioactivity for experiments ranging from a few months to a few years duration and with reasonable safety precautions they can be handled routinely.

Olson (1968) and Odum and Kuenzler (1963) have described suitable methods for measuring the movement of radionuclides from primary producers to other components of the ecosystem. Much work remains to be done which will demonstrate the transfer of nutrients from primary and secondary producers to microorganisms.

PURPOSE

This exercise is designed to acquaint the student with the handling of radioactive tracers and their use in nutrient cycling studies; other exercises emphasize additional uses of various isotopes.

MATERIALS AND EQUIPMENT

Microecosystems of various ages and axenic cultures of certain components of these ecosystems
^{65}Zn in solution
^{54}Mn in solution
Pipets
Propipet or pipeting bulbs
5 established microcosms of various ages
Filter holders
Membrane filters—0.45 μ X 25 mm
Plastic or rubber gloves—disposable
Blotting sheets
Flasks
Counting device—planchet or liquid scintillation counter
Liquid scintillation vials

PROCEDURE

Microcosms are especially suited for this exercise on nutrient cycling since radioactive substrates are retained in the container rather than released into the natural habitat.

In this exercise the radioactive materials will not escape from the system but will be found in either the particulate or soluble fraction. Therefore, only a limited amount of tracer needs to be added to the system.

1. Inoculate new microcosms or use older systems with the ages known.
2. Dilute ^{65}Zn and ^{54}Mn and add to the microcosms according to these directions. (More stringent regulations may be imposed in the student laboratories according to the discretion of the instructor.) Mark work area with warning signs.
   a.   Radioactive Zn and Mn should be stored in lead containers in a protected area.

b. These materials should be handled carefully; always wear rubber gloves and hold the stock solution away from the body. Do not allow the stock solution to come in contact with the skin. Wash thoroughly with soap and warm water after handling.

c. Cover the lab bench and work area with sheets of absorbant paper; place a waterproof layer next to the bench surface.

d. While pipeting always use a propipet—never suck on the pipet with your mouth nor touch it to your skin. Be careful not to spill stock solution on the floor or work area.

e. Via pipet transfer a small amount of the stock solution to a larger amount of distilled H_2O in a well-marked flask. Mix the Zn and Mn in separate flasks.

f. Pipet 0.1 ml of diluted Zn and Mn to scintillation vials and count for 1-5 minutes. This solution should have sufficient counts so that when added to the microcosm that system will have approximately 500 CPM/ml. Therefore, 1.0 ml of a solution of 5×10^4 CPM/ml may be added to 100 ml of microcosm and the final solution will have nearly 500 CPM/ml. Be certain to check the final solution.

g. Add comparable amounts of ^{65}Zn and ^{54}Mn to separate microcosm flasks. Check CPM/ml and record on flask and in your notebook.

h. Carefully clean the work area. Rinse pipets at least twice and store the rinse water in the storage jars provided. These storage jars should be clearly marked with appropriate warnings and always stored in an out of the way, safe place until disposal. Pipets can be washed as usual after rinsing.

i. Paper from work area should be carefully folded, placed in a plastic bag and stored in a safe place for future disposal. (The disposal of these materials is the concern of the instructor and the campus health safety officer. Prior to disposal the radioactivity of the items should be checked.) Monitor the work bench, floor and workers using a portable counting device. If excess (above background) radioactivity is apparent the area should be rewashed and rechecked.

3. Each group now has an equal number of microcosms containing approximately 500 to 1000 CPM/ml, depending on the final concentration.

4. Incubate these systems under normal growth conditions.

5. At selected times, at zero time and daily thereafter, withdraw 1.0 ml of each well-mixed microcosm and filter on 0.45 μ filters. When filtering small amounts it is best to first pipet 5-10 ml of H_2O or buffer in the filter funnel and then add the 1.0 ml of sample. This procedure results in a more even distribution of the sample on the filter and less quenching of the radioactive material by a physical overlay of particles.

6. A number of factors affect the reliability of counts of radioactive substances; the amount of interference due to too much material on the filter, the placement of the filter in the vial or planchet, the efficiency of the counting device, the size of the opening or window through which the light or electrons pass and the overlap of peaks of highest counts when two or more radioactive substrates are in the same sample.

Accurate counting of the substrates used in this exercise may be impossible under most student laboratory conditions. It may be valuable for the student to compare relative counts in the same microcosm over the successional period.

7. Remember that the half-life of these substrates is relatively short and that natural disintegration will take place during the study period. The half-life is the length of time required for one-half of the radioactivity to disappear. Half-life of ^{54}Mn is 312 days while that of ^{65}Zn is 245 days.

Questions

1. Which tracer was taken up by the living organisms in greater amounts?
2. Do young systems assimilate more Zn than older cultures? Mn?

3. This exercise tells very little about the turnover times of these nutrients. How might these procedures be modified to clarify the uptake and release rates?

4. This type of exercise is of value for learning the relative amounts of incorporation of the elements by systems of different ages and diversity. It may be of interest for you to compare the uptake of ^{65}Zn and ^{54}Mn by cultures of 1, 2 or 3 species of bacteria and algae. Which culture would you expect to incorporate the most isotope? Why? What differences between cultures would account for different rates of uptake?

DATA SHEET

Tracer Techniques

CPM

Sample number	Age	Filter R 1	R 2	R 3	Filtrate R 1	R 2	R 3

Results and Discussion

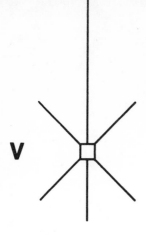

V

Ecological Energy Flow

Objectives of this unit are (1) to demonstrate that energy flows through ecosystems, moving systematically from one population to others within the laws of thermodynamics, and (2) to show methods by which the energy movement may be measured. The measurement of energy by these methods is not as refined as most scientists and engineers may hope for. More elaborate procedures are available in many instances, but have often not been adapted to ecological studies. Data from these exercises will provide estimates of energy flow which should prove to be valuable in ecological investigations.

The ultimate source of energy on earth is the light and heat of the sun. Primary producers utilize light energy during the process of photosynthesis. Unused energy dissipates and is lost as heat. A portion of energy assimilated by the plant may be measured as the photosynthetic product. Primary producers lose energy as CO_2, heat, and via ingestion by herbivores. Primary consumers, i.e., herbivores or members of the second trophic level assimilate a part of the ingested material, excrete a portion and lose the remainder as waste and heat. Assimilated and retained energy may be measured as biomass and temperature increase. Thus, at every trophic level some energy is retained and some is lost. Ultimately, organisms at each trophic level die and the energy remaining is passed through the ecosystem via decomposer action.

Energy in ecological systems is commonly measured in calorie units. Quantitative determinations of energy movement from one trophic level to another can be made. Ecologists often accept the following general estimates of ecological efficiencies: 1% of sunlight is utilized by primary producers and approximately 10% of the energy available at any specified trophic level may be assimilated by the next single trophic level. The remainder of the energy is lost as heat or waste and is not assimilated by the consumer. These figures are gross estimates and ecologists are beginning to take exception to both the figures and methods of estimating these trophic efficiencies.

Each ecosystem may have more or less efficiency of energy utilization than the next. Ecologists are now trying to determine energy flow through all types of systems. It should be emphasized that energy does not cycle but flows through the system once and cannot be recycled. Part of the duty of microbiologists is to remind ecologists that microorganisms are extracting unmeasured amounts of energy from primary producers and consumers at every trophic level. Suitable methods must be devised for measuring the energy which flows into microorganisms.

Coincidently with the study of energy flow we may be able to clarify food webs of the ecosystem, determine the efficiency of the system and thereby make the best use of the land or habitat under study; subtle interactions may be observed which would be overlooked otherwise. Through these studies it may be possible to develop planned, zoned ecosystems in which man is a member rather than the master. Energy flow studies must not be totally theoretical, for there are definite ways to apply this knowledge.

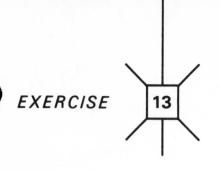

EXERCISE 13

THE MEASUREMENT OF STANDING CROP BIOMASS

The standing crop biomass is the amount of organic matter present in a given system at a given time. A common method of measuring the standing crop of a terrestrial or aquatic system has been to mark off m^2 areas and clip the above-ground vegetation. Too often this clipped material is termed "autotrophic production" or primary productivity. Errors in estimating photosynthetic activity by the clip method arise with failure to: (1) include the plant root biomass, (2) measure the losses to herbivores, (3) determine the loss of plant excretions to leaf and rhizosphere microorganisms, and (4) account for the energy utilized by the plants for metabolism, growth, and development.

Odum (1959) defines primary productivity as the *rate* at which energy is stored by photosynthesis and chemosynthesis of producer organisms. . . . ; he further emphasizes that standing biomass and primary productivity should not be equated. Gorden (1969) has postulated that carbon losses to microorganisms during the growing season may result in an underestimation of the productivity via the harvest method. As an aid in the clarification of terms, Westlake (1965) offers an excellent discussion of terminology and criteria for productivity data.

The amount of standing crop biomass present has little value as the sole measure of the productivity of an ecosystem. However, changes in biomass and in populations are valuable means for estimating productivity if measurements are made often enough. As an example, a deciduous forest may have more biomass per hectare[2] than the same area of a cornfield and still be less productive than the cornfield. In order to determine the rate at which energy is stored in a growing plant, animal or microbial biomass, one must know the initial amount of biomass and thereafter measure increases at sufficiently short intervals so that little of the biomass produced is lost to predators, respiration, and emigration.

In aquatic systems accurate measurements of microbial and phytoplankton productivity are virtually impossible with present methods. The determination of the productivity of aquatic vascular plants is equally difficult. Evidence is accumulating that aquatic vascular plants excrete organic compounds into the water of the littoral zone. The concentration of these compounds may vary 2 to 5 fold during a 24 hour period. These excretions are thought to be utilized by epiphytic bacterial populations as well as being dispersed throughout the pelagic zone (Harold Allen, personal communication). The measurement of standing crop is a vital first step when estimating aquatic productivity.

PURPOSE

To consider the changes in dissolved and particulate organic material as important measurements when estimating aquatic ecosystem productivity.

METHOD

Beginning at zero time and at regular intervals thereafter, representative samples of the system are taken, and the ash-free dry weights measured. If possible, the per cent carbon of the sample should also be measured. From these measurements the changes in biomass may be determined and the productivity of the system estimated.

MATERIALS AND EQUIPMENT

Suitable sampling equipment, dependent upon system being sampled
Niskin Sampler, Whirl Pak bags, sterile pipets, clippers, shovels

Filtration equipment—pump, filter holders
Membrane filters 0.45 μ pore size—metal membrane, glass filters, or cellulose-acetate filters
Crucibles—25 ml or larger size
Drying oven—60°C or less
Muffle furnace—400°C-500°C
Balance—accuracy to 0.1 mg
Dessicator
Tongs
5 ml pipets
100 ml graduate cylinder
0.1 N HCl
Optional equipment
    Carbon-hydrogen-oxygen analyzer
    Bomb calorimeter

PROCEDURE

1. Select a suitable sampling instrument and establish sampling stations in a lake, stream, microcosm or terrestrial system.
2. Sample at intervals, considering the turnover time of the populations involved. Turnover time refers to the length of time in which the members of a population develop, die and are replaced by new members.
3. Place samples in sterilized containers, retain at system temperature or below and rapidly transport to the lab.
4. Filter the sample using preweighed, washed, 0.45 μ pore size metal membrane or glass filters. Washing the filters, especially cellulose acetate membrane types, is necessary due to the amount of extraneous organic material which adheres to the filter during their production. Prior to use filters may be washed by flushing with 60 ml of 0.1 N HCl and rinsing with 20 ml of prefiltered distilled H_2O. Particulate organic matter is retained on the filters; dissolved organic matter passes through the filter. (It may be best to take 5 smaller rather than a single large sample to better determine the biomass per volume unit statistically.) For terrestrial systems skip step 4.
5. Place tared filter and particulate biomass in a clean, tared crucible. Record the tare and the system and date. Use tongs when handling crucibles. Place dissolved organic matter in crucibles and handle in a similar manner.
6. Place both crucibles in a drying oven set at <60°C. Avoid spilling and loss of material; also, place lids on crucibles to prevent accidental addition of organic matter.
7. After drying, weigh and record crucible weight.
8. Place crucibles in muffle furnace at 400-500°C for 1-2 hours.
9. Remove crucibles to dessicator for cooling and weigh when cool. Replace in dessicator and reweigh 1-4 hours later. Record weight as ash weight.
10. Subtract ash weight from the dry weight; the final recorded figure is the ash-free dry weight of the particulate and the dissolved biomass of each sample.

By plotting in graph form the ash-free dry weight of the system over a period of time it is possible to note the different phases of ecosystem net productivity.

Supplementary Exercise

1. Store aseptically filtered, soluble organic matter under refrigeration (frozen, if possible). This material may be analyzed at a later date to determine per cent organic carbon using a dissolved carbonaceous analyzer.[1]
2. Dried particulate biomass may be analyzed to determine the per cent of organic carbon using a particulate carbon, hydrogen and nitrogen analyzer.[2]
3. Measure water volume of the system to estimate productivity/liter or m^3.
4. Of particular interest is the calorie value of organic matter of a system. Particulate and liquid components of an ecosystem may be measured using a bomb calorimeter. An exercise is included in this manual for these determinations although a bomb calorimeter[3] may not be available in most biology departments.
5. Changes in the concentration of reduced compounds in a cell, organism or community will be reflected in the changes in the caloric values of the biomass. Lipids are the most common highly-reduced compounds produced in nature. The basic structure of lipids is a carbon-hydrogen chain. The caloric value of fats per gram dry weight is approximately double that of proteins and carbohydrates. Therefore a system which is accumulating energy is likely to store some energy in lipids and thereby contribute to a total increase in the caloric value/gram of the ecosystem.

In the author's laboratory the changes in total lipids, free fatty acids and saponified fatty acids have been measured during successional stages in an aquatic system. Preliminary data show that distinct changes are apparent in lipid concentrations of both the dissolved and particulate fractions (Lowry and Gorden, unpublished data). Further investigation is required to reveal the importance of the various fatty acids as regulators of community metabolism at the ecosystem level.

Questions

1. List some of the problems involved in securing an accurate sample of the primary producers from the ecosystem you selected. Were epiphytic organisms present? Had tissue been eaten from leaves and stems of vascular plants? Were you able to secure all of the root biomass?
2. What time interval seems appropriate for sampling the system selected? How did you estimate the generation time and turnover time of the important organisms?
3. What suggestions do you have for improving and refining the procedures in this exercise?
4. Suggest ways in which the energy flowing from the primary producers to microorganisms can be more accurately measured.
5. Plot on graph paper the changes in particulate and dissolved ash-free dry weight, caloric values and per cent of carbon in the samples.

---

1. Equipment available from Beckman Instrument Company.
2. Ibid.
3. Adiabatic O_2 Bomb Calorimeter, available from Parr Instrument Company, 211 Fifty-Third Street, Moline, Illinois.

DATA SHEET

Standing Crop Biomass

		Particulate biomass Dry weight					Dissolved biomass Dry weight		
Sample	Filter and crucible	Biomass	Ash	Dry-weight ash-free	Crucible	Biomass	Ash	Dry-weight ash-free

DATA SHEET

Carbon Content

	Soluble			Particulate		
Sample	Dry weight	Carbon	Percent carbon	Dry weight	Carbon	Percent carbon

Caloric Value

Pellet weight	Temperature increase	Wire burned	ml titrated	Calories/gram

STANDING CROP BIOMASS

Results and Discussion

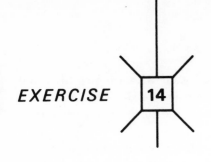

RADIOACTIVE TRACER STUDIES

Mixed populations of bacteria, phytoplankton and zooplankton can assimilate radioactive substrates in the lab or in nature, and axenic cultures of these ecosystem components are able to do the same. It should be possible to culture these organisms, expose similar populations to the isotope and determine their ability to take up substrates *in vitro*. A comparison of the total uptake by the various components with the uptake by the ecosystem may be interesting.

If axenic cultures assimilate substrates and respire $^{14}CO_2$ and release ^{14}C-organic compounds, we may be able to follow these to other system components under certain conditions. This information should aid us in clarifying pathways of the carbon cycle in nature. As an example, we have previously noted the work of Hobbie and Crawford (1969) which indicates that large percentages of the ^{14}C aspartic acid and glucose are respired by bacterial populations during the incubation period. If algal cells were present they might utilize the $^{14}CO_2$ photosynthetically and thereby be shown to benefit directly by association with the bacteria. This could be demonstrated readily in class by the use of a U-tube with a 0.10 μ filter between a tube containing bacteria labeled with ^{14}C-aspartic acid and another tube containing unlabeled algal cells. As $^{14}CO_2$ is respired by the bacteria it would pass freely through the filter and into the algal chamber. After a suitable incubation time the algal cells could be measured for ^{14}C uptake.

This exercise proposes a dual-purpose study designed to (1) note differences in uptake of a radioactive substrate by cultures of bacteria of different ages, species and population size; and (2) to determine whether filtrate from the labeled cultures could be utilized by other populations.

MATERIALS AND EQUIPMENT

Same as for other exercises in this section
Vortex mixer
20-30 ml screw cap test tubes
Culture tubes
Taub 36 media, half-strength
10 U-tubes, if available
0.10 μ filters
Dialysis tubing

PROCEDURE

1. Select 5 dominant species of bacteria from a lake or microcosm. Purify the cultures and inoculate 6 capped tubes of each in 15.0 ml of H-Taub media.
2. Grow the cultures for 1, 2 and 3 days under suitable growth conditions.
3. After 24 hours select 2 tubes of each species and withdraw 1.0 ml of culture for plate counts and/or microscopic counts.
4. To the remainder of the culture add 0.5 μc of ^{14}C-U-Glucose suspended in 1.0 ml of sterile H-Taub.
5. After 30 minutes incubation time, withdraw 0.1 ml or 1.0 ml of the culture, filter and count the radioactivity of the sample.
6. Quickly centrifuge the remaining sample, decant the supernatant and resuspend the pellet in 10 ml of sterile H-Taub.

7. Transfer the bacterial pellet and 10 ml of Taub to one side of a U-tube with a $0.10\,\mu$ filter and inoculate the other side with an unlabeled species of bacteria suspended in H-Taub liquid.
8. After an incubation period of 4-6 hours, filter 1.0 ml or more of the cultures on each side of the U-tube and compare the radioactivity.
9. If no U-tubes are available, place the radioactive culture in dialysis tubing and suspend the tubing in the second culture in a way that materials could pass from the tubing into the culture liquid. Or, incubate the labeled culture for 4-6 hours, centrifuge and pipet 1.0-2.0 ml of the supernatant into a series of sterile tubes containing 2.0 ml of sterile H-Taub.
10. Inoculate these tubes with fresh unlabeled cultures of each of the 5 bacteria.
11. Incubate for 4-6 hours, filter the bacteria, count for radioactivity and estimate the amount of movement of radioactive carbon compounds from 1 population of bacteria to another.

Questions

1. If the bacteria inoculated into the supernatant in step 10 fail to show an uptake of radioactivity, what may be the reasons?
2. What method could you use to show that ^{14}C-organic compounds were present in the supernatant?

DATA SHEET

Tracer Studies
Exercise

Sample number	Age	CPM	Size of Population/ml	Growth in the supernatant by bacteria and CPM				
				A	B	C	D	E
(Ex.)1 A	24 hr.	$5.0 \times x10^3$	5×10^5	25	70	695	30	63

TRACER STUDIES

Results and Discussion

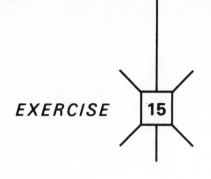

GROWTH IN FILTRATE OF OTHER CULTURES

Following the growth of bacteria in nutrient broth, sufficient nutrient may remain to support populations of other species of bacteria. What portion of the organic material was endogenous and what fraction was excreted or released by the initial population? The answers to these types of questions will help answer questions concerning the succession of dominant bacterial types in mixed populations. Such questions as (1) Can species B survive in media in which species A lived? Is the pH suitable? Are the nutrients depleted? Were toxins produced? and (2) If species B cannot survive, can species D. C. E. . . . N? If so, why?

In this exercise a simple growth test procedure is suggested which may help explain why some organisms are dominant or more abundant than others in a mixed population.

MATERIALS AND EQUIPMENT

Culture tubes and flasks
0.45 μ filters and equipment for filtrations
H-Taub media or suitable substitute
Spectronic 20 or other optical density equipment
Angle head centrifuge

PROCEDURE

1. Select 5 bacteria capable of growing in the H-Taub or other selected media.
2. Inoculate and grow these cultures for 1, 3 and 5 days in tubes or flasks; 125 ml flasks would be best.
3. After 1, 3 and 5 days of incubation, centrifuge the cells into a tight pellet; discard pellet, filter the supernatant aseptically using 0.45 μ filters and dispense the filtrate to sterile culture tubes. Cap and label the tubes.
4. Inoculate the filtrate in the tubes with each bacterial culture in a separate tube.
5. Make optical density readings of each culture at zero time and daily thereafter for 5 days.
6. Plot the growth curves on graph paper.
7. You have grown a series of bacteria on the filtrate from growing cultures of each other bacteria. Which organisms can use the filtrate and which cannot?
8. Algae from the system may be cultured on the filtrate in the light, also. Growth factors supplied by the bacteria may enhance the algal growth. One may determine algal growth increases by chlorophyll determinations, optical density measurements or direct microscopic counts.
9. The author used these methods to demonstrate the influence which bacteria of the microcosm have on the *Chlorella* growing therein (Gorden et al. 1969). In that case the *Chlorella* showed a requirement for the vitamin, thiamine, which was produced by a number of the bacteria. *Chlorella* grew better in bacterial filtrates than in H-Taub alone. However, the *Chlorella* grew best when grown in the same tube or flask with certain bacteria.
10. You may wish to repeat the experiments described in the paper mentioned or devise your own using other organisms.

DATA SHEET

Growth in Filtrate

Growth of

in optical density units in filtrate of:
these samples

Sample	Own filtrate	A/species	B/species	C/species	D/species	E/species

GROWTH IN FILTRATES

Results and Discussion

LOSSES FROM PHYTOPLANKTON TO CONSUMERS

In this exercise we will use a slightly different approach to determine losses from primary producers to consumers. *Chlorella* sp., when growing *in vitro* and *in vivo,* are capable of excreting many organic acids and substances such as amino acids and carbohydrates. These same cells will reassimilate certain of these materials which have been "stored" outside of the cell. The *Chlorella* of our microcosm will take up large amounts of labeled glyoxylate and probably other substrates. We will capitalize on this characteristic to try to find a part of the food chain or web of the microcosm system.

MATERIALS AND EQUIPMENT

Radioactive substrates
 ^{14}C-U-glyoxylate
 ^{14}C-U-glucose
 ^{14}CO$_2$ or Na ^{14}CO$_2$
Radioactive counting equipment
Liquid scintillation counter
Angle head centrifuge
Filter, membrane, pore size 0.45 μ or less
Membrane filtering equipment
Pipets, glassware as needed for labeling procedure
Screwcapped test tubes

PROCEDURE

1. Add 1.0 μC of labeled substrate suspended in 1.0 ml of Taub 36 A to screwcap test tubes and store in refrigerator until needed.
2. Warm the tube and suspension to ambient temperature and add 1.0 ml of concentrated *Chlorella* cells. (*Chlorella* may be isolated, grown in pure culture in suitable media, spun down via angle head centrifuge, washed, centrifuged and resuspended in a small volume of autotrophic Taub 36 media.)
3. Incubate suspension for an appropriate length of time under light growth chamber conditions. Appropriate conditions vary with the labeled substrate. Glyoxylate apparently moves in and out of the cells with little restriction. Cells may reach an equilibrium within 1 to 24 hours.
4. Following incubation, cells may be washed carefully and aseptically 3 times using sterile, autotrophic Taub. After the final washing resuspend the *Chlorella* cells in 1.0 ml sterile A-Taub and add the labeled cells to the selected microcosm.
5. The microcosm may be mixed so that the *Chlorella* cells are well distributed throughout the system.
6. Immediately, at zero time, a 1.0 ml sample of the mixed microcosm should be aseptically removed and filtered, rinsing with 2.0 ml of A-Taub media. Thus, the amount of radioactivity in the dissolved and particulate portion of the microcosm may be determined initially. Place the filter in a liquid scintillation counting vial (called vial) and add 1.0 ml of the filtrate to another vial.
7. At selected intervals 1.0 ml samples of the mixed microcosm should be extracted, placed in

small screwcap tubes and 1.0 ml of 10% formalin added. Suggested time intervals are: 1, 5, 10, 15, 30, and 60 minutes, every 2 hours for the next 24 hours and every 12 hours for 1 week. Each sample should be carefully marked and saved for careful study using radioautographic techniques.

8. At the same interval 1.0 ml of the sample should be filtered, dried and counted in the isotope counter. The amount of radioactivity remaining in the particulate matter is of interest.

9. Macroscopic animals, such as Ostracoda and other Crustacea, may be selected individually at each sampling time. These may be checked for radioactivity by placing an individual in a vial and placing in the liquid scintillation counter.

Alternative Suggestion

Pure cultures of bacteria of the system may be labeled in the same manner and added to the system. Difficulty will be encountered in determining whether other species of bacteria have taken up the label from substances released by the labeled bacteria. It would be possible, however, to determine if the label had been assimilated by algal cells or by heterotrophic animals.

Name_____·_____ Section _____ Date _____

DATA SHEET
Losses from Phytoplankton

Age	Sample number	CPM	7 days	Radioautographic results	1 month

91

Results and Discussion

NEMATODES ON FUNGAL MATS

Approximately 10,000 species of Nematoda have been described but it is probable that many more species are unknown (Hutchinson 1967). Marine, freshwater and soil, free-living and parasitic species of nematodes have been studied. When considering the abundance and diversity of this group it seems improbable that the Nematoda ecology is not better understood.

Nematodes are nonsegmented invertebrates ranging from 1.0 mm to 5.0 mm in length. Many are microscopic since magnification is required for best viewing. Two major head types are known; (1) those with mouth parts which are detritus feeders, and (2) others with a hollow, hypodermic needle-like stylet which are plant parasites.

Isolation of nematodes from aquatic and terrestrial habitats is relatively easy when using flotation methods, seine-sifting methods or fungal mat procedures. Following isolation one may culture the organisms on nutrient agar plates using additional substrates. Procedures described in this exercise are based on methods developed by Meyers and Hopper (1966) and on personal communication with these workers. Although these methods were developed for marine nematodes they are suitable for isolation from most habitats.

MATERIALS AND EQUIPMENT

Soil screens or sieves—decreasing mesh sizes
Table top centrifuge and tubes
Dissecting scope
Microscope
Petri plates
Nutrient agar
Pipets—5 ml
Cellulose mats
Wooden stakes
Plastic face plates
Mesh screen
Small screws

PROCEDURE

I. Flotation-filter method

1. Secure sediment or soil sample.
2. Mix sample with water (seawater).
3. Pour through gradient screens.
4. Rinse with filtered water (seawater).
5. Repeat steps 1-4—three times.
6. Using material retained on the screen proceed to no. 7.
7. Make a sugar-water mixture using Karo syrup.
8. Fill tube 1/2 full of sugar-water and pipet or place 5.0 ml of sample on surface of each tube.
9. Remember to balance tubes prior to centrifugation.
10. Centrifuge at approximately 2000 rpm for 3-5 minutes.
11. Pellet of larger organisms will be near bottom of tube—Nematodes in syrup.

12. Filter nematodes from syrup and wash with water.
13. Place nematodes on a nutrient agar plate with a small fungal mat.
14. Observe nematodes and fungi under microscope or dissecting scope.
15. Note mouth parts and feeding habits of the nematodes.
16. Certain fungal species form hyphae into loops which may tighten around a nematode as the animal passes through the loop. In these cases the food chain is reversed and the fungi become hunters and consumers.

II. Fungal Mat Method

1. Grow fungal mats on cellulose pads in the laboratory. Meyers and Hopper (1966) used the marine fungi *Dendyrphiella arenaria* Nott and *Halosphaeria mediosetigera* Cribb & Cribb in their work. The fungi were grown on 0.1% Bacto-Yeast Extract in Gulf Stream seawater with cellulose pads added to the liquid. Similar methods may be employed in the culture of freshwater fungal species of your choice.
2. Develop a method or use this method for exposing the fungal mats to the nematodes in the water.
3. Drill holes in the stakes approximately the same size as the cellulose-fungal mats.
4. Place the mesh screen and the face plates over the mats and bolt or screw in place using stainless steel bolts or screws.
5. In a similar fashion place controls consisting of two cellulose mats together in the water.
6. Following a suitable exposure period of 1-5 days the mats may be viewed under a dissecting microscope.
7. Note the numbers of males, females and gravid females. Also, make observations on the feeding habits of nematodes.
8. By placing mats at different depths in the littoral region of a lake or ocean some additional information regarding colonization by the nematodes may be gained.

Questions

1. Were there differences between the nematode species colonizing the different species of fungi? at the same depth in different locations? at different depths in the same location?
2. What conclusions can be reached regarding the feeding habits of the nematodes which you have isolated?
3. Would you expect to find seasonal variations in the dominant species?
4. Do nematodes feed on bacteria? Devise an experiment which will demonstrate that bacteria can support nematode growth.

DATA SHEET

Nematodes and Fungi

Day Month Year
___ _____ ____

Sample	Substrate fungal sp.	Inches Above Surface	Males	Nematodes Present Females	% Gravid	Mouth Parts	Observations and no. of species

Results and Discussion

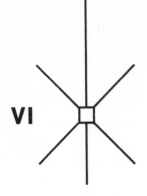

VI

Community Metabolism and Decomposition Studies

Communities consist of interacting populations of various types of organisms within a given ecosystem. Communities may be large or small and may be either autotrophic or heterotrophic in nature. In the community individuals and populations grow and die, using and releasing gases as they carry on normal metabolic activities. Metabolism may be referred to as the total of the physiological functions of particular organisms. In this instance, the emphasis is placed on the measure of gaseous exchange which is a reflection of the total metabolic activity of the organisms or community.

Community metabolic activity may be compared to that of an individual. An autotrophic community, like a photosynthetic plant, carries on photosynthesis and respiration. If the system is growing in size and productivity the photosynthetic phase must surpass the respiratory phase, i.e., the P/R ratio must be greater than 1. If, instead, the system is not productive the P/R<1 or in equilibrium P/R = 1.

Heterotrophic communities are always operating at a P/R deficit. Such systems are dependent upon input of detritus and living organic matter in order to maintain life. Cave ecosystems, areas below the photic zone of lakes and oceans and soil systems may be so classified.

For measurements of community metabolism one may utilize methods suitable for individuals. However, usually some modification of methods must be made. As an example, a small aquatic system may be sampled and using Warburg manometric methods the photosynthetic and respiratory capabilities of the system may be measured. Expanded manometric-type methods have been developed for larger systems. Witkamp (1966b) and Reiners (1968) have enclosed portions of the forest floor in air-tight containers and noted the difference in the CO_2 content of the air passing in and out of the containers. H. T. Odum and coworkers enclosed a part of a Puerto Rican rain forest in a huge plastic cylinder 60′ high by 150′ in diameter. A large motor pulled air into the cylinder and out the bottom. The changes in O_2 and CO_2 content of the air were measured.

Beyers (1963) and others have utilized the pH-CO_2 method to measure the community metabolism of small aquatic systems. Odum (1957) measured the metabolism of Silver Springs, Florida via a modified light-dark bottle method featuring bell jars. The literature is filled with methods and data of experiments on community metabolic rates. This section will detail a few methods suitable for measuring community metabolism.

An important part of any community is the group of organisms which is actively reducing the organic components of the ecosystem to their basic elements. These organisms are commonly called "decomposers" and may consist of various types of worms, insects, certain vertebrates and microorganisms. Heterotrophic organisms of all types aid in the decomposition of organic matter (note Section III).

Decomposition is the process of separating a substrate into its components. Biological decomposition consists of a series of enzymatic and, often, mechanical activities which result in the complete oxidation of the substrate. During this degradation, the energy and carbon have passed through a series of decomposer trophic levels, the ecosystem has undergone an ecological succession and the biomass and caloric values of the system have changed.

Microorganisms compete successfully for dead organic substrates. When a plant or animal dies the ubiquitous microflora initiate the attack by utilizing the most easily assimilated proteins and carbohydrates. Depending upon the environment, invasion by other bacteria, actinomycetes and fungi follows. Specialists which have enzymes capable of utilizing cellulose, hemicellulose, chitin and other difficult-to-degrade substrates may be the final members in succession. During the decomposition process macro- and microinvertebrates may have been ingesting and reingesting the decomposing materials, eating microorganisms and maintaining the decomposers in an exponential growth phase (Johannes and Satomi, 1966). According to Englemann (1961) soil arthropods affect fungi in at least three ways: (1) they feed on the fungi; (2) they expose fresh substrate to the hyphae and spread spores through the substrate; and (3) they grind the large detritus particles, moistening and mechanically degrading the organics, and egest much of the material exposing more surface area to fungi and bacteria. Gorden (1969) has outlined the movement of energy through the decomposer fraction of a soybean field.

Since macrodecomposers influence the rate of decomposition of natural substrates their activities should be measured separately from those of the microdecomposers. Exercises 18 to 23 are adapted from methods of Crossley and Hoglund (1962) and Witkamp (1963, 1966a). These exercises illustrate ways in which a significant portion of the metabolic activity of certain communities can be measured separately from other components.

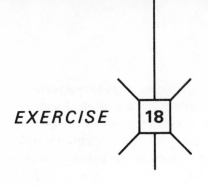

EXERCISE **18**

MEASUREMENT OF COMMUNITY METABOLISM

Estimates of the productivity of aquatic ecosystems can be made using modifications of the pH-CO_2 method. This method is based on the fact that as the concentration of CO_2 in the water changes, the pH of the system also changes. As the community respires in the dark, the increased CO_2 in the water results in a pH decrease. Photosynthetic activity decreases the CO_2 and a pH increase takes place. Thus, daytime net production (P_n) and nighttime respiration (R_{ni}) can be measured. The difference between these two values is related to the productivity of the system.

The highest pH readings (due to CO_2 changes) are expected in late afternoon and the lowest in early morning just prior to sunrise. By taking pH readings of the water twice each day at the peak pH period, comparing the pH reading with CO_2 saturation charts for that temperature and by subtracting R_{ni} from P_n one may determine community metabolism.

Lee and Hoadley (1967) offer an interesting discussion of chemical equilibria of aquatic systems.

MATERIALS AND EQUIPMENT

pH meter—expanded scale
Assorted beakers, flasks
A series of established microcosms
Tank of CO_2 gas and regulator valves
Buret
Magnetic mixer and mixing bar

PROCEDURE

1. Establish microcosms in the growth area. Note light and dark periods. In growth chambers the light-dark periods are known and definite, whereas in nature a gradual change in day length takes place. Or, select a suitable natural habitat for the study.
2. Take pH readings of the series of microcosms or of the lake at each sample site. A number of microcosms or sample areas should be used to provide a range and mean of the pH. Determinations of pH should be made at the time of the high and low pH periods. Record pH for each flask or sample site.
3. By bubbling CO_2 via airstone or in other ways into distilled water, the pH of the titration H_2O can be lowered to pH 4.4 or lower. This CO_2-water, in a buret, may be used to titrate the microcosm or lake water.
4. Periodically, (every few days during rapidly changing successional phases) using the microcosm with the highest pH or water at highest pH period, titrate 100 ml of the system using saturated CO_2-water.
5. Record the pH change for each of 0.2 ml CO_2-H_2O added per 100 ml of sample.
6. Record the temperature of the microcosm or water sample.
7. Beyers et al. (1963) have published a table from which pH-CO_2-temperature correlations may be derived.
8. By comparing the day and night pH measurements, a curve can be constructed which shows the productivity of the system.
9. Record the results as mM CO_2/liter.

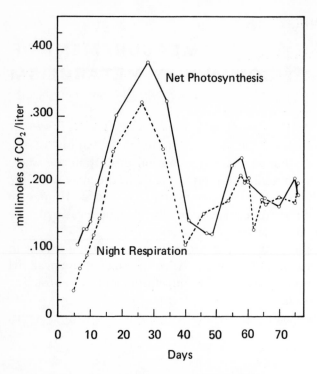

Figure 18-1. Microcosm Community Metabolism

Reproduced by permission of Gorden R. W.; R. J. Beyers, E. P. Odum and R. G. Eagon, 1969. Studies of a simple laboratory microcosm: bacterial activities in a heterotrophic succession. *Ecology* 50: 86-100, Figure 8, p. 98.

10. By making a series of pH measurements and titrations over a period of time the resulting curves will indicate the productive stages of the system. Plot R_{ni} and P_n curves on graph paper as seen in Figure 18-1.

Questions

1. What are the most likely sources of error inherent in this method?
2. Some workers have suggested that the titration should be made using acid rather than CO_2-saturated water. Why is the acid titration less likely to be accurate? What are the problems inherent in CO_2 titrations?
3. What are the carbonic species commonly found in fresh water? How is each affected by the photosynthesis—respiration activity of the community?
4. Relate the influence of the buffering capacity of the water to the community metabolism measurement method of this exercise.

DATA SHEET

Community Metabolism

Sample	Age	pH				titration	
		AM	PM	AM	PM	ml	mMCO$_2$/liter

To Do:
1. Plot the standard curve
2. Prepare R_{ni} and P_n curves

Results and Discussion

CARBON DIOXIDE EVOLUTION BY SOIL COMMUNITIES

The evolution of carbon dioxide from soil has too often been used as a measure of microbial activity in soil. Due to the many types of organisms present in the soil it is not a valid measure of microbial activity. We may, however, consider it a measure of community respiration from the soil. Witkamp (1966a, 1966b) has devised a simple method of measuring the CO_2 evolution from the forest floor which may be adapted to other soil communities. When one considers this as community respiration it must be remembered that if photosynthetic plants are present in the area being measured a light-dark box method must be used in order to separate light and dark respiration. Secondly, the length of incubation time must be determined empirically. If possible, this method should be correlated with methods described for decomposition of confined and unconfined substrates. Amounts of CO_2 present in a system may be measured using a CO_2 analyzer, a CO_2 probe or by the KOH absorption methods.

MATERIALS AND EQUIPMENT

20 clear plastic, bottomless boxes—approximately 15 cm × 10 cm × 6 cm
20 screw capped, wide mouthed, 30 ml capacity glass jars
1 titration burette
1 magnetic stirrer and small mixing bar
0.2 N KOH solution
0.179 N HCl solution
Saran wrap or plastic film
10 light-tight boxes or covers to place over the respiration boxes

PROCEDURE

1. Select a typical, suitable habitat in which to place the boxes.
2. Boxes should be sunk approximately 2.5 cm into the soil by cutting around the edge with a spatula or knife. Care should be taken not to disturb the soil excessively.
3. Boxes may be placed at random or in a prescribed pattern and may be installed permanently or temporarily. Readings may be taken as often as seems necessary to gain a fair estimate of community activity. Following installation, a period of one hour may be allowed for equilibration of the system. Boxes should be left open except when measurements are to be made.
4. In the laboratory or field add 5-10 ml of 0.2 N KOH to each widemouth glass jar and cap tightly.
5. Transport these jars to the boxes; uncap; place one jar in each box and immediately cover the box tightly with the plastic film.
6. Incubate for 1 to 2 hours.
7. Remove the plastic film; cap the KOH jar and transport to the laboratory for titration.
8. Titrate each jar, as soon as possible, using 0.179 N HCl.
9. CO_2 evolution rates may be plotted as $ml/hr/cm^2$.
10. Confined and unconfined litter may be placed in plastic boxes (with bottoms) and estimates of CO_2 evolution and of decomposer activity made in the same manner on the basis of dry weight of the substrate. Note: if photosynthetic algae, vascular plants or photosynthetic bacteria are

present in the system, boxes must be covered to exclude light during the "dark" phase of the exercise.

11. By combining this exercise with those for decomposition compare CO_2 evolution rates with decomposition rates.
12. In addition, counts of fungi and bacteria present on the leaf litter may reveal interesting successional changes when conducted over an annual period.

Witkamp (1966b) noted rates ranging from 0.75 to 1.50 ml/hr for 175 cm^2. He then estimated that 1440 ml of CO_2 were evolved for each gram of litter which was decomposed.

Questions

1. Why is soil respiration, as measured in this exercise, not a valid estimate of soil microorganism respiration?
2. Do plant roots respire? Might that CO_2 be included in the community respiration? What happens to CO_2 evolved in soil and mud?
3. Why will the method described not work in aquatic systems?
4. What methods of measurement of CO_2 are suitable for aquatic studies?

DATA SHEET

Soil Community Respiration

Sample		Titrant	CO$_2$ evolution	Organisms present	
Number	Size, cm^2	ml	ml/hr/cm^2	Number	Type

Results and Discussion

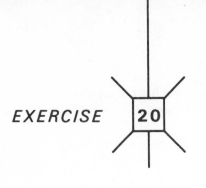

EXERCISE 20   THE LIVING SEDIMENT

The sediment of a lake, stream or of the ocean is an integral component of the ecosystem. In this sediment, whether sand or mud, is a living community. The type of community present depends upon the type of water, availability of light and numerous other chemical and physical factors. Just as the water phase may change with depth, so may the sediment form a gradient from the mud-water interface to >90 cm deep.

The top 5-10 cm of the sediment may be well aerated and agitated by the turbulent waters above. Below 10 cm there may be microorganisms and invertebrates capable of living at low O_2 concentrations or of moving to the surface for O_2. In anaerobic areas the Eh and pH may prevent the growth of all except anaerobic bacteria specifically adapted to the rigorous conditions.

Inorganic reactions which affect the pH/Eh relationships of aquatic ecosystems delimit the habitats in which microorganisms can live (Baas Becking, Wood, and Kaplan 1957). These reactions are: (1) oxidation and reduction of sulfur compounds; (2) oxidation and reduction of iron; (3) the buffering capacity of the medium as controlled by the $CO_2 - HCO_3$ and CO_3 relationships; and (4) photosynthesis, a process utilizing CO_2 and releasing O_2 or removing hydrogen. These reactions influence the sediments, as well. Wood (1965) provides a clear and interesting account of the ecology of marine environments and the pH-Eh limits of microbial growth.

The sediments offer an interesting field of study. Leo and Parker (1966) have found branched-chain fatty acids in several marine sediments. The structures isolated suggest a bacterial origin for these branched-chain isomers. The sulfur and iron microorganisms are commonly active in the sediments. Photosynthetic bacteria may be functional during a major portion of the year.

Winogradsky columns (so called since they were used by one of the great, early microbial ecologists) can be used to demonstrate the presence of green and purple sulfur bacteria, diatoms and algae in the sediments.

MATERIALS AND EQUIPMENT

Hollow, transparent plastic tubes or corers—1" or 2" in diameter
Corks of suitable size to fit the corers
Aluminum foil
Light source

PROCEDURE

1. Sterilize the corers and corks while enclosed in paper.
2. Transport the corers and corks to the sediment to be sampled.
3. Unwrap the plastic corer and insert it into the water and straight into the sediment.
4. Insert the corer smoothly into the sediment for 1/2 to 2/3 of the length.
5. Place the cork in the upper end.
6. Withdraw the tube filled with water and sediment.
7. When the bottom is clear of the sediment place the cork in the bottom and return the core to the shore or boat.
8. Repeat this procedure in approximately the same spot.
9. This entire procedure is great fun if carried out while snorkeling in Florida Bay. However, a field trip to that location is not a prerequisite for this exercise.
10. Wrap aluminum foil around one corer and leave the other open to the light.

11. Transport the Winogradsky columns to the lab and place both in the lighted area.
12. After 1 day note that colonies of microorganisms increase in size. Observe and mark the locations of the main colonies.
13. Note that different types of microorganisms are dominant at different depths and in relation to the amount of light available. Compare the two cores.
14. The Winogradsky column may be used for many measurements and isolations.
    a. pH, Eh, O_2 may be measured using appropriate electrodes.
    b. Sulfur oxidation, sulfate reduction and photosynthetic activities may be observed.
    c. Sulfur bacteria, photosynthetic bacteria, diatoms and other algae may be isolated.
15. The column may be as simple as described or may be more elaborate with ports at graduated levels for periodic sampling. In any event much can be learned by appropriate experiments and observations of Winogradsky columns from different habitats.

Questions

1. Suggest a procedure which will insure that the colonies which develop in the column are forming at the depth at which they were found in the sediment.
2. Design an ecological experiment which will measure the rate of an ecological function in progress in the core.
3. List the differences between the sample in the core and the sediment in the normal habitat.
4. Using isolation and enrichment methods described by Aaronson (1970), which microorganisms could be isolated from your column? Make a list of these types. Speculate on the probable ecological importance of each.

DATA SHEET

The Living Sediment

Light	Dark	pH	Eh	O$_2$	Depth	Number of colonies	Bacterial types	Colonies and bacteria

Results and Discussion

EXERCISE 21

THE USE OF LITTER BAGS TO MEASURE DECOMPOSITION OF NATURAL SUBSTRATES

The method described is similar to that used in decomposition studies of the International Biological Program (IBP) Grassland Biome. Purified cellulose strips and blue-stem hay are used for comparative decomposition rates at many study sites. In addition, investigators are measuring decomposition and changes in caloric values of the grasses which are dominant on their own study area. In the IBP an objective is to compare rates of functions and energy flow in the different types of ecosystems in the U.S. and the world.

MATERIALS AND EQUIPMENT

Plastic or collodion bags
Nylon or fiberglass mesh bags, plankton netting 10.0 dm^2 $\times$ 1.0 mm, 2.0 mm and 5.0 mm mesh
(obtainable from cloth shops)
Rose bengal stain
Glass slides
Petri dishes
Dilution bottles
90% alcohol
Media—nutrient agar, Actinomycete isolation agar, Saborouds agar
Stainless steel nails
Scales—Mettler balance or comparable balance
Filters and filter holders
Drying oven

ALTERNATE EQUIPMENT

Magnetic stirrer
Microscope with integrating eyepiece
Bomb calorimeter
Muffle furnace

PROCEDURE

1. Select representative fresh substrate (plants, including roots; animals, including chitinous exoskeletons) samples and wash free of inorganic matter. Sufficient quantities should be dried at less than 60°C and approximately 2.5 gm dry wt placed in each mesh litter bag.
2. Determine beforehand the number of mesh bags of each pore size required for the experiment. The length of the experiment may be estimated by existing conditions and class requirements. Most situations suggest a period of 6-12 months as suitable duration for decomposition. The class may wish to place extra litter bags which will be retrieved by classes of following years.
3. Litter bags of 1 mm, 2 mm and 5 mm mesh sizes are suggested. Gradations of various mesh sizes may be advisable when determining the activities of invertebrates of different sizes.
4. Litter bags should be placed on the soil surface, under the litter and in the top 6 cm of soil. Sufficient bags should be placed for monthly retrieval of duplicate samples. Control bags of collodion containing alcohol-sterilized substrates may be placed for monthly retrieval also. Thus, non-biological decomposition may be measured. Note that this exercise calls for

111

cooperation between lab partners and lab groups since the analysis of decomposition is concentrated in a short time period.

5. When bags are retrieved for measurement the contents should be carefully washed, preferably in a strainer or container of small pore size. It may be necessary to filter badly decomposed portions on filter paper or metal or glass filters. After washing the sample should be dried at <60°C and weighed. Rates of decomposition of particulate materials may be determined by the changes in dry weight biomass with time.

6. Types and numbers of bacteria present may be estimated by using dilution plate count methods and various media selective for fungi (Rose Bengal Saborouds), actinomycetes (Actinomycetes Isolation Agar), cellulose digesters (powdered cellulose agar) and other microorganisms.

7. A comparison of the biomass remaining in the litter bags of different mesh sizes will indicate the relative influence of different organisms on decomposition rates.

8. Caloric values of the decomposing substrates may be determined.

Glass slides placed in duplicate bags a few days prior to harvest may be studied microscopically and the length of mycelia measured in order to give an estimate of fungal growth rate.

PROCEDURE

1. Place duplicate glass microscope slides in bags 1 week prior to harvest, making certain one flat side of each slide is in contact with the leaves.
2. At harvest remove slides, stain with rose bengal and observe.
3. Witkamp (1966a) advises that mycelial growth on the slide surface be recorded as the number of intersections (bits) of mycelium with six parallel lines of an integrating eyepiece scanning 16 random microscope fields and using a 10X objective and a 10X eyepiece.

Dilution Plate Method:

Microbial and fungal populations densities may be estimated as follows:

1. Place 1.0 gr of detritus in 100 ml of sterile water and stir for 15 minutes with a magnetic stirrer or chop in a Waring blender for 2 minutes.
2. Follow the dilution pour plate procedure.
3. Modifications of this procedure may be made depending on the type and condition of decomposing strata. Standardization of the method will be beneficial in comparing counts.

DATA SHEET

Decomposition

Number	Age	Bag mesh size	Initial dry weight	Final dry weight	Weight loss	Bacterial counts gram	Caloric value

Results and Discussion

EXERCISE 22

A LITTER BAG METHOD:
DECOMPOSITION IN AQUATIC SYSTEMS

Decomposition of plant biomass is often responsible for lowering the dissolved oxygen in the depths of lakes and reservoirs. Phytoplankton blooms and aquatic vascular plant growth may decrease the light penetration, thereby causing the death of photosynthetic plants which fall to the bottom of the lake and decay. Eutrophication of aquatic ecosystems inevitably results in increased decomposition and lowered oxygen levels in deep water. Thus, anaerobic decomposers are predomiant in these areas.

MATERIALS AND EQUIPMENT

M. and E suggested for Exercise 21 and that suggested for anaerobic bacteria culture, Exercise 1.

PROCEDURE

1. Representative samples of particulate matter present in or near the water may be selected; for example, clumps of blue-green and green algae, vascular plants from different plant zones, leaves and twigs from nearby trees and even phytoplankton may be concentrated via centrifugation or filtration.
2. Sufficient quantities should be washed free of inorganic matter and living fauna, dried at <60°C, weighed and placed in mesh litter bags. Nylon bags of mesh size less than 1 mm should prevent entry by macroscopic aquatic insects. Gradations of mesh size may be advisable when wishing to determine the activity of animals of various sizes in decomposition. Phytoplankton net materials from 60 μ pore size are available.
3. Litter bags may be suspended in the water at various depths from surface to sediments.
4. Sufficient bags should be placed for monthly retrieval of duplicate samples.
5. Control bags of collodion containing alcohol-sterilized substrates may also be distributed.
6. When bags are retrieved for measurement the contents should be carefully washed, preferably in a strainer or container with small pore size. It may be necessary to filter badly decomposed portions on filter paper or metal or glass filters.
7. After washing, the sample should be dried at <60°C and weighed.
8. Rates of decomposition of particulate materials may be determined by the changes in dry weight biomass with time.
9. Directions for processing the litter bag contents are essentially the same as described in Exercise 21.
10. Anaerobic bacteria probably present may be isolated and cultivated using accepted procedures.

Alternative or Supplementary Exercise

Known amounts of substrates may be placed in flasks in the laboratory and sufficient water and sediment from the habitat added. Flasks may be incubated on shakers or stationary, at constant or fluctuating temperatures and with or without light. With flasks of sufficient size, litter bags may be suspended as in the natural habitat.

Alternate Exercises

Caloric values of the decomposing substrates may be measured using the methods described for the bomb calorimeter (see appendix). Carbon-nitrogen (C-N) values may also be measured. Some investigators may wish to measure protein changes of the detritus as well.

Cooperating with entomologists on this exercise will provide a more complete analysis of decomposition processes.

Questions

1. List the probable sources of experimental error in this exercise.
2. How may an investigator successfully follow the energy flow through the decomposition food web?
3. Can you suggest biochemical analyses which may yield a more accurate description of decomposition?

DATA SHEET

Decomposition in Aquatic Systems

Number	Sample Mesh Size	Location	Initial weight Bag	Initial weight Organics	Harvest weight Bag	Harvest weight Organics	Decomposition rate Wt loss	Decomposition rate Gr/day

117

Results and Discussion

EXERCISE 23

DECOMPOSITION OF
UNCONFINED SUBSTRATES

A common method of determining the metabolic potential of some of the microorganisms of natural systems is by determining the rate of decomposition of a substrate. By adding a known amount of the substrate to the system at time zero and then analyzing the system for that substrate at regular or measured time intervals, the rate of removal is established. Dissolved organic substrates may be measured by chemical or biological assay while ash-free dry weights of particulate substrates are often measured. There are inherent problems in either method and the choice of methods is usually determined by the experiment in progress. Often an end product is more easily measured than the original substrate.

MATERIALS AND EQUIPMENT

Purified shrimp tail chitin or other purified solid
Mettler balance
Nylon thread
5-250 ml flasks

PROCEDURE

Decomposition of chitin in aquatic systems.

1. Select a small piece of purified shrimp tail chitin and weigh it carefully. Record.
2. Attach a thread to the chitin and suspend it in the microcosm, natural habitat or culture of pure or mixed bacteria.
3. During the following days and weeks observe the chitin and after approximately 4 weeks remove the chitin from the liquid, wash carefully, and dry it.
4. Weigh the dried material; the difference between the initial weight of the substrate and the final weight represents the loss. Determine the decomposition rate in g/day.

A similar procedure might be used for many particulate substances.

Questions

1. How does one remove the algal and bacterial cells from the substrate?
2. What can be determined from a weight gain?
3. How would you keep the larger organisms from aiding the degradation process?
4. To what extent are higher animals active in decomposition of chitin, starch and other solids?

DATA SHEET

Decomposition of Unconfined Material

No.	Sample Location	Type of substrate	Initial weight	Harvest weight	Weight loss	Decomposition rate

Results and Discussion

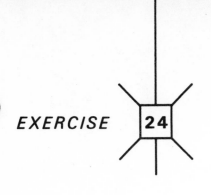

EXERCISE 24 | DECOMPOSITION OF DISSOLVED ORGANIC MATERIALS

A set procedure is practically impossible for such an exercise. However, methods of analysis of many organic materials are available and will be useful in the lab of any microbial ecologist. Alexander (1964) refers to biochemical analyses of substrates in his fine review, p. 239.

The chromatographic methods, including paper, thin layer and gas-liquid chromatography, are very useful when separating the end-products and remaining initial substrate from the other organic substances of the system. The use of autoradiography and other means of detecting uptake of radioactive substrates has been useful in determining decomposition of various substrates.

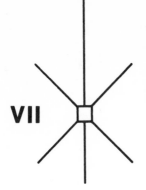

VII

Eutrophication, Ecology and Pollution Control

Much of the pollution of aquatic ecosystems of the world is due to the increasing input of nitrates and phosphates from domestic, industrial and agricultural sources. The exercises of this section offer a means of studying the cycling of these nutrients in the system and the contributions that the microorganisms make to their concentration in the ecosystem.

Eutrophication is the process of enrichment of aquatic systems by the addition of nutrients. A nutrient-poor, unproductive lake is termed "oligotrophic," while a nutrient-rich, highly productive lake is said to be eutrophic. Eutrophication as a natural process is slow and the enrichment may require thousands of years. In populated areas, due to human activities, only a few years may be required to bring a lake to advanced stages of eutrophication. Cultural eutrophication, a term emphasized by Hasler (1969) in an excellent paper on the topic, is reversible. A concerted effort by dedicated and interested citizens is required to eliminate the causes of eutrophication.

Algae require nutrients, vitamins and other growth factors for luxuriant growth. Nitrogen and phosphates are commonly present in runoff from commercially fertilized agricultural land. Sewage and feedlot wastes contribute additional growth-promoting ingredients. Regardless of the source, increased concentrations of N, P and other nutrients stimulate the growth of phytoplankton, epiphytes and other aquatic plants. Bloom conditions result in plant growth only on the lake surface since light cannot penetrate deep into the water. Plants below the shallow photic zone die, decompose and contribute to the depletion of O_2 in the depth of the lake. Due to O_2 depletion, most insects, fish and other animals die; even many bacteria are not capable of surviving in a system devoid of O_2 and are replaced by anaerobic species. Anaerobic decomposition is slow, produces H_2S and other gases and results in incomplete oxidation of organic matter. If eutrophication is allowed to progress, the end result is a system devoid of oxygen, capable of supporting only anaerobic bacteria and populations of undesirable, toxin-producing algae. Finally, the basin will fill and another aquatic system will have been destroyed.

Various other forms of pollution are known to disrupt aquatic ecosystems. Pesticides, toxins, acids, chemicals, oil, hot water from industrial cooling systems and radioactive wastes have been poured, pumped and spilled into marine and freshwater habitats. In many instances, due to the quantity and type of pollutant, microorganisms are not able to degrade these substances, and the water is unfit for most life. The extent to which they affect an ecosystem and its components may be studied using the microcosms mentioned in Section II and the chemostats described in Exercise 25. A few techniques which may be of further aid to the investigator in the study of pollution and its affect on aquatic ecosystems are supplied in the appendix.

Under certain conditions, polluted and eutrophic systems can be used to the advantage of man for the production of food. However, in most cases man will not benefit from the pollution and he must contribute in any way possible to the improvement of the environment in which we live.

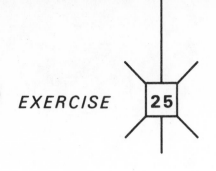

EXERCISE 25

CHEMOSTATS AS ECOLOGICAL TOOLS, CONTINUOUS CULTURE OF BACTERIA

The term "Chemostat" has been applied to laboratory set-ups which include a system designed to provide a growing culture of microorganisms with a controlled inflow of nutrients and a regulated outflow of the culture and waste (Figure 25-1). The idea is to be able to determine the ability of a microbial population to grow in a continuous flow system and to reproduce faster than the dilution rate. Thus, an artificial, competitive situation is established in which, theoretically, only one species is able to survive if the dilution rate is sufficiently rapid. If the dilution rate is slow, two or more populations may survive for a long period of time.

The characteristics of chemostats allow them to be very useful for ecological studies and a series of papers by Jannasch (1962, 1964, 1965) illustrates their value. By manipulation of physical and biological factors of the chemostat the range and limitations of the growth of the populations may be estimated. One may control the temperature, pH, salt concentration etc., and manipulate one variable such as the nutrient concentration or dilution rate. By measuring the changes of the microbial populations passing from the outflow over a given time interval the effect of the variable can be determined. Population changes may be determined by direct or indirect counting methods.

Ecological information which may be derived includes growth rates, release rates of measurable organic acids, vitamins, etc., optimal pH, O_2, CO_2 and growth factor levels. Many ecological conditions can be established and studied. Limitations of the method are due to (1) lack of suitable methods for measurement of excretions and released materials (2) lack of contact between organisms and thereby a lack of interaction due to the one population system and (3) lack of creativeness and ingenuity in experimental design on the part of the investigator. Within the limits of these restrictions excellent work has been and will be done.

Although the basic design indicates a single flask—single culture concept it is possible to add additional culture vessels in a sequence. Thus, by inoculating the first flask with a mixed population a series of flasks may be established with single populations each dependent upon the previous flasks. One may inoculate the vessel with a single population and measure one or more components of the filtrate of succeeding flasks. Either method will aid in clarifying knowledge of the metabolic processes of the microorganisms.

Continuous culture methods can be used for the mass production of a wide variety of organisms and end products (Malek, Beran and Hospodka, 1964). The theories and concepts of both single and multi-stage continuous cultures are discussed in that same symposium. Powell, (1956), Contois (1959) and Herbert, Elsworth and Telling (1956) have presented mathematical approaches to the growth rates and generation times of bacteria in continuous culture. These papers should be studied prior to more elaborate studies using chemostats.

MATERIALS AND EQUIPMENT,

    Taub no. 36 solution, one-half strength (see Exercise 5—Microcosms)

    Glucose

    Proteose peptone

    A variety of substrates

    Equipment for each group of students:

        1 or 2-4 liter Kimax aspirator bottles with tubulature near bottom (may use larger or smaller sizes for reservoir). The reservoir should be large enough to supply the chemostat overnight without interruption

        1 or 2 flat-bottomed flasks or vessels—culture vessels—500 ml flasks overflow receiving flask; tubing and fittings—1/4″ glass, vinyl, tygon or other tubing suitable for autoclaving; glassware similar to that of Exercise 1 and 2; magnetic stirrer and stirring rod

PROCEDURE

    Set up the chemostat according to Figure 25-1 with adjustments necessary for your laboratory. The reservoir should be higher than the desired level of liquid in the culture vessel. Some form of restricting device should be installed in or on the reservoir tubing. A trial run is advised using water in order to determine the turnover time (*see* step 6) of the liquid in the culture vessel and the stirring rate. When a suitable setup has been established proceed with the following steps. Note: This exercise, like many others in this manual, may be modified to suit the local situation. I suggest that the class set up a series of chemostats which are identical except for the type or concentration of substrate. By varying the substrate and using common bacterial types, the influence of one factor on population growth may be emphasized. Later experiments can be designed by the students. Carpenter (1968) has designed an inexpensive chemostat capable of gravity or pump flow, especially designed for the growth of algae in the laboratory.

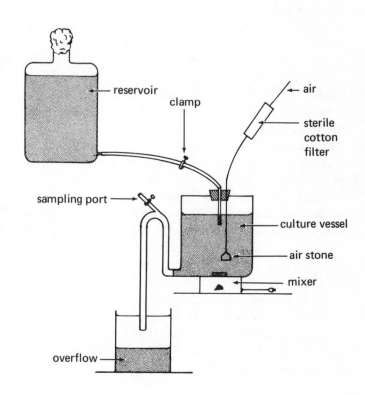

Figure 25-1. A Typical Chemostat

1. One 4 liter bottle or larger carboy should be used as the reservoir. It should contain the basal salts media (Taub 36, one-half strength) plus the desired substrate.

2. Another bottle or flask with suitable overflow at bottom, side or top may serve as the culture vessel.

3. The smaller receiving vessel need not be sterile and is unnecessary if the overflow can run into a sink or larger container.

4. Be certain that proper caps, tubing and fixtures are installed on all bottles and flasks. Prior to autoclaving make sure that all tube ends and caps are covered with bags or paper in order to insure sterility upon removal from the autoclave.

5. Make up the desired amounts and types of media in the reservoir and culture vessels separately. Autoclave for a sufficient time period. Remember that large amounts of liquid require 30-60 minutes for sterilization.

6. Remove containers, set in place, (see Figure 25-1) connect all fittings and allow to cool. While cooling adjust nutrient flow to a dilution rate of 0.03 to 0.5 hr. This rate may be adjusted by closing or opening the restriction device and will be determined as the length of time required to completely replace the amount of liquid in the culture vessel. If the culture vessel contains 2 liters of liquid, an input of 66 ml/min will result in a turnover time of 0.5 hr. The stirring bar should mix the liquid well but not agitate it greatly.

7. Inoculate the culture vessel with the sample. The amount of inoculum necessary will vary with the type of sample and the amount of liquid in the culture vessel. Inocula of pure and mixed cultures of bacteria should be smaller than for samples from a natural habitat; the less extraneous nutrients added the better.

8. Sampling procedure. At zero time and at regular intervals thereafter the microorganisms should be observed. Extract a sample directly from the culture vessel or from the overflow vessel. Bacterial numbers, species diversity and dominant types can be observed using dilution plate counting methods (Exercise 1). Direct counts may be made, also (Exercise 2).

9. Following the inoculation of mixed cultures the population which survives should be the one which can compete for nutrients under the growth conditions imposed. Axenic cultures influence the environment even under continuous culture. Therefore, one should observe the pH, O_2 concentration and other factors regularly during the experiment.

10. Record the changes in population numbers and types along with your observations.

Questions

1. How may the "bottle effect" or wall growth influence bacterial populations in chemostats? Do you feel that this bottle effect will be increased with low dilution rates: With low substrate concentrations? Is the wall growth phenomena found in nature, on rocks and other solid, inanimate objects?

2. Can ecological information be gained from chemostat experiments or is the single culture situation too far from nature? Compare the use of single versus multiple stage chemostats for ecological studies.

3. What are the types of natural habitats which correspond to a chemostat?

4. What modification would be necessary to develop an ecosystem in a single or multi-stage chemostat?

5. How can biochemical studies be used in continuous culture work? What end-products might be measured? What excretions may be monitored under these conditions?

6. You are encouraged to design better chemostats and better ecological experiments involving continuous culture methods.

DATA SHEET

Continuous Cultures

Sample Number	Age	Dilution rate	Bacterial pop/ml Direct	Plate	Diversity	Description of dominant cells

CONTINUOUS CULTURES

Results and Discussion

EXERCISE **26**

MEASUREMENT OF NITROGEN FIXATION BY SOIL AND AQUATIC MICROORGANISMS

For many years the known nitrogen-fixing organisms were the legume-*Rhizobium* group, *Azotobacter* and *Clostridium*. Recent research on biochemical aspects of nitrogen fixation combined with agricultural and pollution-oriented research has demonstrated that the ability to fix gaseous nitrogen is widespread among microorganisms and higher plants.

Stewart (1967) lists 15 bacterial species, 14 blue-green algae and 19 root nodulated vascular plants capable of nitrogen fixation. In addition, lead nodulated nitrogen-fixers are known. Most nitrogen-fixing bacteria are anaerobes, and the aerobes seem to be most efficient in this activity at oxygen tensions below 20%.

The magnitude of biological nitrogen-fixation is great. An estimated 90 million tons of fixed nitrogen per year contributed to the earth's surface is of biological origin (Donald 1960). Legumes fix an estimated 100 to 200 kg of N/hectare per year (Stewart 1967), nonlegumes fix up to 179 kg N/hectare per year (Stewart and Pearson 1967), and blue-green algae in rice paddies may fix from 30-50 kg N/hectare per year (Stewart 1966). Free-living soil organisms fix nitrogen at rates ranging from 0.1 kg to 73.0 kg/hectare per year for anaerobes while aerobic organisms fix up to 34.6 kg/hectare per year (Knowles 1965).

The effect of increased amounts of nitrogen in aquatic systems has drawn the attention of limnologists. Sources of nitrogen in water include agricultural runoff, nitrogen fixation by aquatic microorganisms and nitrification. The latter is a two-phase process involving the bacteria *Nitrosomonas, Nitrosocystis* and *Nitrobacter*. The probable mechanisms are:

Ammonium ions, ammonia or amines

1. $NH_4^+ + 3/2\ O_2 + H_2O \rightarrow NO_2^- + 2H_3O^+$

2. $NO_2^- + 1/2\ O_2 \rightarrow NO_3^-$

These microorganisms are aerobic and autotrophic, and derive their essential carbon by CO_2-fixation. The basic process of nitrogen-fixation is described by the formula:

$$6(H) + N_2 \rightarrow 2NH_3$$

$$ATP \rightarrow ADP + Pi$$

(**Note:** A considerable amount of energy is required for the reduction since N_2 is stable.) Biochemical studies are revealing the necessary enzymes and sources of energy and reducing power for these processes. Nitrogen (fixed) is used in the synthesis of amino acids and hence in numerous cellular components.

It is possible to quantitatively estimate rates and amounts of nitrogen fixed by Kjeldahl analysis, the microdiffusion technique and with the use of isotopes ^{13}N and ^{15}N.

Recently N_2-fixation has been measured as the uptake of ^{15}N as determined using a mass spectrometer. This method is quite sensitive but is time-consuming and very expensive. Based on an earlier discovery that nitrogenase reduces acetylene to ethylene, Stewart et al. (1967) have developed a method for the measurement of *in situ* N_2-fixation. This method has been tested on aquatic and terrestrial systems and apparently may be adapted to many field conditions.

MATERIALS AND EQUIPMENT

2 dozen 5.0 ml glass serum bottles with rubber serum stoppers
No. 22 hypodermic syringe and needles
Hand vacuum pump
Gas-liquid chromatograph with 1/8 in, 9', Porapak R column
Gases—Acetylene (purified grade)
Gas mixture of O_2 (22%), CO_2 (0.04%) and argon (78%, high purity)
Millipore filters (Grade HA)
Filter holders and filtering apparatus
Sterile sampling containers—Whirl-Pak or Niskin sampling bags
Sterile 1.0 ml pipets
Sterile cork borer or soil corer
50% trichloroacetic acid
RTV sealant

PROCEDURE

I. A. *Aquatic systems*
    1. Using aseptic techniques secure a water sample.
    2. Pipet 1.0 ml into each duplicate 5.0 ml serum bottle.
    3. Cap the bottles with the rubber stoppers.
    4. Proceed to Section II.

  B. *Soil or nodule systems*
    1. Using the cork borer or soil corer aseptically obtain a soil sample. It may be necessary to dig up the root system of a legume when obtaining nodules.
    2. Washing the nodules in sterile, distilled H_2O will remove soil particles and adhering bacteria.
    3. Weigh or estimate 100-500 mg fresh weight of soil or nodules and add to each 5.0 ml bottle.
    4. Cap the bottles.
    5. Proceed to Section II.

  C. *Axenic cultures*
    1. In the laboratory pure or known cultures may be added to the bottles in a manner and quantity empirically determined for each system.
    2. Cap the bottles.
    3. Proceed to Section II.

II.
    1. Flush the capped serum bottles by inserting a needle slightly through the serum cap.
    2. Insert a second needle with syringe filled with the gas mixture attached through the cap.
    3. Flush the bottle twice.
    4. Alternately, the bottles may be evacuated using a needle and a hand vacuum pump; this method is not suitable for liquid samples.
    5. Withdraw all needles from the cap.
    6. Inject 0.5 ml acetylene into the sample.
    7. Seal the cap with RTV sealant.
    8. Incubate *in situ* for the desired period; usually 30-60 minutes is a sufficient incubation period.
    9. Inject 50% trichloroacetic acid via syringe to inactivate the system (0.2 ml to water; 0.5-1.0 ml to soil and nodule samples).

10. Seal with sealant.
11. Samples may be taken to the laboratory for analysis of ethylene production.

III. 1. Detect ethylene formation by injecting samples of the air from the serum bottle into a gas chromatograph apparatus fitted with a 9 ft long by 1/8 in dia column containing Porapak R (or comparable column) at room temperature. High purity N_2/flow rate 25 ml/min is a suitable carrier.
2. Sampling conditions may be adapted to the detection equipment available.
3. Samples consisting of water filtered through 0.45 μ filters (Millipore HA or comparable) may serve as controls.
4. Control samples may also be inactivated with 50% trichloroacetic acid prior to flushing and introduction of acetylene.
5. It is necessary that a standard curve of increasing concentrations of ethylene be prepared for comparison with results from various samples. Concentrating, diluting, or decreasing the sample may be advisable.
6. Kjeldahl digestion of the sample will provide a measure of total nitrogen. Protein values may be estimated as total N × 6.25. These values may be used to provide a value of ethylene production/mg protein or total nitrogen.

IV. *Analysis of data*
1. The reproducibility of the method should be checked by measuring the ethylene production of 10 aliquots of a representative sample.
2. Replicates of each sample are also advisable to establish statistical reliability. One may wish to empirically establish the optimum incubation period and sample concentration.

Stewart et al. (1967) have shown a linear response between time and acetylene reduction by root nodules. However, the ratio between acetylene reduction and N_2-fixation is apparently not 1:1. *In vitro* studies resulted in a correlation value of acetylene/N_2 fixation of 1.25 for *Clostridium* and *Aerobacter*. Reduction of acetylene to ethylene requires 2 electrons whereas reduction of N_2 to $2NH_3$ requires the transfer of 6 electrons. Due to the difference between the expected value of 3.0 and the experimental values of 1.25 to 1.59, further work remains to establish reliable values for the method.

Questions

1. What modifications can you suggest for this exercise?
2. Suggest ways to quantitate the method in relation to microbial cells present rather than total biomass of the system.
3. What differences may one expect between light and dark N_2-fixation in photosynthetic organisms? Why? How did your results compare with this reasoning?
4. What differences may be expected in light and dark N_2-fixation in heterotrophic bacteria? Why? Compare with your results.

DATA SHEET

N-fixation
Acetylene Reduction

Sample	Ethylene standard values G-C			Ethylene produced x 1.25 = G-C		Nitrogen fixed/g ml	Total N Kjeldahl x 6.25 =	Total protein
				Rep. 1	Rep. 2			

Results and Discussion

BACTERIAL UTILIZATION OF ^{32}P

The concentration of inorganic phosphorous rapidly declines following addition of fertilizer to freshwater and marine ponds. Long term investigations by F. R. Hayes and his group at Dalhousie University have demonstrated that (1) an equilibrium may be established in which the mud holds a high percentage of phosphorous while the H_2O holds a relatively small amount; (2) vascular plants will compete successfully with the mud for inorganic phosphorous; and (3) bacteria, when present, assimilate most of the ^{32}P while the plants and mud acquire little. Hayes and Phillips (1958) suggest that the high concentrations of ^{32}P in the water in the presence of bacteria may be due to two activities, (1) acceleration of the rate of ^{32}P returning from the sediment to the water by bacteria of the mud; and (2) conversion of the inorganic ^{32}P to organic phosphate compounds which do not participate in the inorganic mud-water equilibrium. These workers have illustrated the transformations of inorganic PO_4 and estimated turnover times for natural and artificial aquatic systems.

Radioactive phosphorous (^{32}P) is an energetic beta-emitting isotope with a half-life of 14.3 days. Consideration of the short half-life is important in measuring. The relatively short half-life makes this isotope suitable for use in natural ecosystems and it has been used extensively in both marine and freshwater systems. However, this isotope must be handled with caution.

Johannes (1965) found that bacteria alone regenerate very little dissolved inorganic phosphate (DIP), but bacteria and marine protozoa together regenerate more DIP than they would separately. He attributes this increase to a greater consumption of detritus by bacteria which are maintained in an exponential growth phase by the predator protozoans. The DIP in the bacterial cells is released as the cells are digested by protozoa.

This exercise is designed to demonstrate the effect of bacteria on regeneration of DIP in an aquatic system.

MATERIALS AND EQUIPMENT

^{32}P inorganic phosphate
0.45 μ filters and filter holders
25 ml volumetric flasks
Butanol-reagent grade
Acid molybdate
Citrate
Selected antibiotics
Pure bacterial cultures
Silica cell
Vascular aquatic plants
Methanol
Cuvettes
Spectrophotometer
Liquid scintillation counter or other radioisotope counting device
Centrifuge—capacity to hold 250 ml bottles
Centrifuge bottles—250 ml

PROCEDURE

1. Select mud and water samples from appropriate aquatic systems; secure at least 20 ml of mud.
2. Place the samples in sterile 250 ml centrifuge bottles and centrifuge the mud to the bottom. (If only smaller tubes and centrifuge head are available use them and combine the sample parts.)
3. Decant the supernatant water and add 100 ml filter-sterilized lake water to each bottle.
4. Allow bottles to incubate one week, in the dark, so that the systems reach an equilibrium.
5. Bottles may be treated as follows:
   a. Mud and water
   b. Mud, water and 15 mg of antibiotic tetracycline
   c. Mud, water and a small, vascular, aquatic plant
   d. Mud, water, vascular plant and 15 mg of tetracycline
   e. Mud, water and added bacteria, 2 ml at 1×10^7/ml
   f. Mud and water autoclaved or steam sterilized
6. Allow all bottles to reach equilibrium after adding the treatments listed.
7. Dilute the dissolved inorganic phosphorous (DI ^{32} P) in sterile lake water. (Please use the necessary safety measures.) Adjust the dilution so that approximately 5×10^5 CPM/ml are registered on the counting device.
8. Add 1.0 ml of the DI ^{32}P solution to each bottle. This will result in a final dilution of approximately 5000 CPM/ml in each bottle.
9. Incubate the bottles, in the light, for the duration of the experiment.
10. At zero time and at selected intervals thereafter follow this suggested sampling procedure.
11. Withdraw, via pipet and propipet, 1.0 ml of water from the bottle.
12. Filter the water through a 0.45 μ filter.
13. Flush with 5.0 ml of 5% formalin.
14. Bacteria are impinged on the filter. DIP is in the filtrate.
15. Dry the filter and place on a planchet for counting.
16. Place 1.0 ml of the filtrate in a planchet, dry and count. Remember the dilution factor.
17. Vascular plants may be sampled at the same time, dried, ground, weighed and counted in a like manner.
18. Mud samples may be carefully taken by pushing a glass tube 1 cm into the mud, closing the upper end and lifting the mud to a planchet.
19. Decant or pipet water from the mud; dry, weigh and count.
20. Sampling times may vary with the system. However, note that bacteria-water equilibrium is reached within five minutes whereas 1-5 days may be required in mud-water systems.
21. Differences expected from this exercise may be estimated from previous studies. Bacteria should take up the majority of the isotope and slowly release it to the mud as dead cells reach the sediment and decay. Vascular plants should assimilate more isotope in the absence of bacteria than in their presence.
22. It may be valuable to determine total phosphate of the samples being tested. A colorimetric method is described in the appendix.

Questions

1. Explain why bacteria assimilate and hold phosphorous. What are the compounds which contain P in the cells? Where might P be held in a "storage form" within the cell as organic but inactive P-compounds? as inorganic P?
2. From an ecological sense what is the importance of the information gained from this type of experiment?
3. Account for the differences of ^{32}P in the water (filtrate) between the sample bottles.
4. Compare your results with data provided by other groups.

DATA SHEET

Utilization of ^{32}P

Sample	Min time	Mud	Counts/min		Plants	Total P	Additional Information
			Filter	Filtrate			

Results and Discussion

APPENDIX 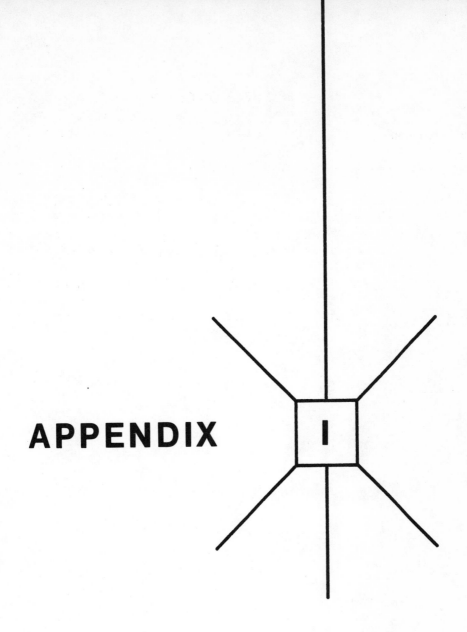 I

Microorganism and Humans

Intensive studies of interactions between macroorganisms and microorganisms have involved the intestinal flora relationships and the bacterial activities within the human mouth. The importance of such studies is obvious even though the ecological approach may not be as apparent.

The human organism (ecosystem) supports large populations of microorganisms both externally and internally. It is impossible to produce a sterile human mouth under normal conditions. Using antibacterial substances the flora can be reduced in number and effectiveness. The importance of bacteria in dental caries and the diversity of diseases of the jaw, nose and throat emphasizes the need for continued study. When disease-causing organisms become established they are able to reduce the metabolic and ecological efficiency of the host. The amount of energy taken from the host by the bacterial populations and the reduction of assimilation efficiency are two areas in which the ecological approach might be used.

Intestinal flora may contribute vitamins and aid in the digestion of certain foods. The contributions of these populations is difficult to measure. On the basis of gnotobiotic (germ-free) studies of other mammals one may extrapolate to the human. Under certain conditions various organs of germ-free animals are enlarged and growth factors are required in their diets. Also, the use of antibiotics may eliminate bacteria from the intestinal tract indiscriminately, resulting in detrimental effects on human health. These general statements are intended only to point to significant areas of ecological research.

Energy flow through the human ecosystem is of the utmost importance. The capacity of the human body to survive on reduced amounts of food and to adapt to dietary changes may be in part dependent upon the microflora of the body. In fact, the human population of our world may soon be dependent upon the protein from algae, bacteria and other microorganisms as a supplement to the diet.

Externally, the human microbial population is as numerous, diverse and interesting as are the ecological niches of the skin. Marples (1969) has compared the areas of the human body to desert, forest and grassland ecosystems of the world. Although the surface of the human is an unstable environment, beneficial, harmful and pathogenic microorganisms are able to survive. Succession, diversity, dominance and the niche are ecological concepts which are indirectly applicable in the skin communities. Many microorganisms growing in and on the skin have distinct physiological and cultural requirements.

In short, humans and microorganisms are compatible and together represent a system of great ecological interest.

Rumen Microbial Ecology

Ruminants, those cloven-hoofed cud-chewers, are animals of definite ecological importance. The ruminants and the rumen microbial populations live together in a symbiotic relationship. As plant materials in the rumen are digested and fermented, acids and gases are produced. Acids are absorbed and utilized by the host while the CO_2 and methane gases are excreted. The protozoa and bacterial cells are utilized as food, as are many of their growth waste products.

Hungate (1966) states that the favorable growth conditions of the rumen permit diversity in the populations of bacteria and protozoa as well as a concentration of individuals as great as in any other natural habitat.

Growth conditions in the rumen are fairly constant, representing a moving chemostat or continuous fermentation chamber. In contrast to the single culture encouraged by chemostat conditions a series of differences allows the rumen to support diverse populations. Ruminants have a complex diet, thus microorganisms of the rumen may be adapted to a narrow ecological niche or may be capable of using many different substrates. Those microorganisms which are most efficient in the use of the substrates are also most likely to thrive. As the populations become established, the various niches are narrowed and changed by these same populations—thus, creating new niches. These factors all contribute to the species diversity.

Rumen microorganisms are mainly obligate anaerobes although aerobic bacteria may be present. On a hay or forage ration, gram-negative bacteria dominate; with grain in the ration, gram-positive cells increase. Cocci and short rod forms are most common. Total numbers may range as high as 4.0×10^{10}/ml of rumen fluid by direct count.

The functions of rumen microorganisms include the digestion of cellulose, hemicellulose and starch, sugar fermentation, and the utilization of lactose. Of course, proteolytic and lipolytic bacteria are present. Acetic acid is the fermentation product produced by the greatest number of rumen bacteria. Propionate or butyrate are formed by 25% of the rumen species. Rumen microorganisms may synthesize large quantities of riboflavin, pantothenic acid and Vitamin B_6 while small amounts of thiamine, niacin, biotin and certain other vitamins are produced in the rumen.

Rumen bacteria can be cultured in anaerobic media under transfer and incubation conditions as anaerobic as possible. Various media have been developed which (1) simulate the conditions of the total rumen and thereby support a number of species, or (2) media which simulate a specific rumen niche and support only 1 or 2 rumen species may be used.

Suggested procedures for isolation and culture of rumen microorganisms are offered by Hungate (1966) in an excellent book which has served as the source for the above information.

Although much research has been completed on rumen microorganisms there are areas in which little information is available. The ecological relationships of bacteria and protozoa are worthy of intensive study. The protozoa, mainly ciliates, actively digest cellulose and ferment sugars. It is highly likely that they feed on bacteria since bacterial numbers are greater in the absence of protozoa.

An exercise for the ecological study of rumen microorganisms is not within the scope of this manual since most laboratories are not equipped for such experiments. Individuals may wish to design their own investigations after thoroughly studying the source material.

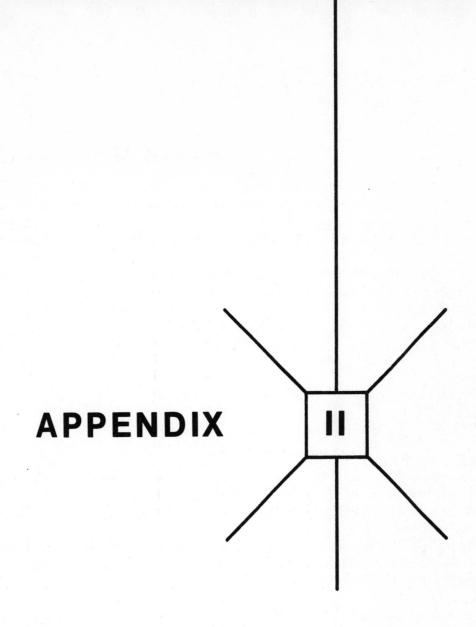

APPENDIX II

Phosphate Determinations

Due to the key role of various forms of phosphorous compounds in eutrophication of natural waters, a knowledge of the concentrations of these compounds has become extremely important in microbial ecology. Three forms of phosphorous are of interest: (1) inorganic orthophosphates, (2) inorganic polyphosphates, and (3) organic phosphorus or the total phosphorus content minus the inorganic phosphates. Phosphorus may be termed soluble or insoluble depending upon its passage through a filter of a specific pore size, usually 0.45μ.

Many methods of determination of phosphorus have been used in the past. These exercises are based on the work of Jankovic, Mitchell and Buzzell (1967) and Harwood, van Steenderen and Kuhn (1969a, 1969b). The methods are relatively simple, straightforward, rapid, consistent and sensitive. They depend upon photometric measurements and are useful for a range of waters from oligotrophic systems to sewage waste waters. Measurements may be made in the field or laboratory.

Determination of Orthophosphate in Water

This procedure is based on the formation and reduction of phosphomolybdic acid by an acidic molybdate solution containing ascorbic acid. On reduction a blue color is formed after 10 minutes and remains stable for 24 hours.

MATERIALS AND EQUIPMENT

Reagents: (Use reagents of A.R. grade, where possible)

4 N H_2SO_4—Concentrated sulphuric acid (112 ml) is slowly added to 800 ml distilled water. After cooling, the solution is diluted to 1 liter with distilled water.

0.96% molybdate—Ammonium molybdate 0.6 grams $(NH_4)_6 Mo_7O_{24} \cdot 4 H_2O$ crystals are dissolved in distilled water, with heating. On cooling, the solution is diluted to 1 liter with distilled water.

10% ascorbic acid—10 g powder are dissolved in 80 ml distilled water and diluted to 100 ml final volume. This reagent should be stored in a cold room (2°C) when not in use, and made fresh on the development of a noticeable color.

Tartrate—The solution is made to contain 1 mg Sb/ml, by dissolving 0.667 g of potassium antimony tartrate ($KSbO \cdot C_4H_4O_6$) in 250 ml distilled water.

Mixed reagent—Equal volumes of the ascorbic acid and the tartrate reagents are mixed before use. This is prepared fresh as required.

Glassware for each group:

1—50 ml volumetric flask for each sample

5—5 ml pipets

propipets

Photometric instrument set at 890 mμ

Sampling device—non sterile

PROCEDURE

1. Secure a suitable sample, 10-40 ml or less, mix and pour into the 50 ml volumetric flask.
2. Add 5.0 ml of both the sulfuric acid and ammonium molybdate reagents, using the propipets provided.

3. Swirl the flask to mix the water and reagents.
4. Add 4.0 ml of the mixed reagent to the flask; shake and mix well.
5. Dilute flask contents with distilled H_2O to 50 ml.
6. Allow at least 10 minutes for color to develop; color may require 30 minutes to develop in cold weather, i.e. $10°C$, as compared to $25-30°C$ summer temperatures.
7. Read in photometric device at 882 and 890 mμ.
8. Compare optical density of samples with the standard curve developed from data of measurements using 0 to 150 μg P/50 ml controls.
9. The total amount of orthophosphate in the sample will be indicated by the O.D. standard curve. The amt/ml can be determined by dividing this amount by the number of ml in the initial sample.

Measurement of Total Phosphates in Water

Total phosphates may be measured quickly and quantitatively in the following manner:

1. Secure a representative sample of the aquatic habitat being studied. The sample should be cooled prior to analyses if transportation to the lab is required.
2. If soluble and insoluble phosphates are to be separated, 50-100 ml of the sample should be filtered through 0.45 μ filters, 45 mm dia. Soluble phosphate may be determined by analyzing the filtrate. Insoluble phosphates will be retained by the filter.
   a. To measure insoluble phosphates wash the filtered material from the filter using 50 ml of distilled H_2O; resuspend by swirling, shaking or blending.
3. Treat each of the two portions of the sample separately, but in the same manner as described here.
4. Place 10 ml of the sample in a 125 ml Erlenmeyer flask. Add 2.0 ml of sulfuric acid, 1.0 gram of $K_2S_2O_8$ and dilute with 30 ml of distilled water.
5. Add boiling beads and boil for about 15 minutes. Place a small funnel in the flask mouth to prevent evaporation loss.
6. Cool, rinse funnel and flask and dilute to 500 ml using distilled H_2O—(note final dilution).
7. After cooling and dilution, add 8.0 ml of the mixed reagent to a tube or flask and dilute to 50 ml with dilute treated sample.
8. Allow a minimum of 10 minutes for color development and observe absorption at 890 mμ. Determine phosphate concentrations using calibration curve prepared by using standard phosphate solution.

Further analytical procedures for phosphate determinations are based on the work by Jankovic, Mitchell and Buzzell (1967).

MATERIALS AND EQUIPMENT

Filter equipment
Membrane or glass fiber 0.45 μ filters
Large test tubes which fit into the filtering flask
Glassware—acid-washed with 1:1 HCl and rinsed repeatedly with distilled H_2O
Reagents:
   Sulfuric acid, 5 N—Dilute 140 ml of concentrated H_2SO_4 to 1 liter with distilled H_2O.
   Ammonia molybdate—Dissolve 40 grams of $(NH_4)_6MO_7O_{24} \cdot 4 H_2O$ in distilled H_2O and dilute to 1 liter. Store in Pyrex container.
   Ascorbic acid, 0.1 M—Dissolve 1.32 grams of ascorbic acid in 75 ml of distilled H_2O. Prepare at the time of use.

Potassium antimonyl tartrate, 1 mg Sb/ml—Dissolve 0.2743 grams of potassium antimonyl tartrate in distilled H_2O and dilute to 100 ml.

Mixed reagent—Mix thoroughly 125 ml of 5 NH_2SO_4 and 37.5 ml of molybdate solution. Add 75 ml of ascorbic acid solution and 12.5 ml of tartrate solution. Prepare as needed.

Standard phosphate solution, 0.5 mg P per ml—Dissolve 2.1954 grams anhydrous KH_2PO_4 in 1000 ml distilled water.

PROCEDURE

I. Immediately prior to removal of sample, aliquots should be mixed and blended thoroughly.

II. Orthophosphate determination
1. Filter 50 ml of the sample through 0.45 μ filter.
2. Dilute 5.0 ml of the filtrate to 100 ml with distilled H_2O.
3. Place 8.0 ml of the mixed reagent in a 50 ml tube; Add 42 ml of the diluted filtrate; Mix.
4. Allow 10 min for color development.
5. Observe absorption at 822 mμ. Record.
6. Establish calibration curve for known concentrations of standard phosphate solutions.
7. Determine phosphorus content of the sample by comparison with the standard phosphorous curve.

III. Total inorganic phosphorus
1. Place 20 ml of the blended sample in a 125 Erlenmeyer flask and add 1 ml 5N H_2SO_4. Dilute with about 25 ml distilled water.
2. Add several boiling beads and boil sample for 15 minutes. A small glass funnel inserted in the mouth of the flask helps prevent loss of sample.
3. Cool the flask in water and transfer contents into a 500 ml volumetric flask. Rinse the flask and small funnel with distilled water and fill to the mark. Note that this corresponds to a dilution of 25 times rather than 20 times as used in step II. 2.
4. Repeat steps 3 through 7 of the orthophosphate determination.

IV. Total phosphorus
1. Place 10 ml of the blended sample in a 125 ml Erlenmeyer flask.
2. Add 2.0 ml 5 N H_2SO_4 and 1.0 gram potassium persulfate, $K_2S_2O_8$, and dilute with about 30 ml distilled water.
3. Add boiling beads and boil for about 15 minutes. A small funnel may be used as in step III. 2 preceding.
4. Cool the flask contents and dilute to 500 ml with distilled water. Note that this corresponds to a dilution of 50 times.
5. Repeat steps 3 through 7 of the orthophosphate determination.

Bomb Calorimetry

Ecologists are becoming more interested in the movement of energy through ecosystems. Energy is converted, assimilated, stored and lost by individuals, populations and communities. This energy, as heat, can be measured by various methods. The oxygen bomb calorimeter is a useful tool for the measurement of the caloric value of combustible materials in solid or liquid form.

Caloric value, expressed as cal/gram or BTU (1 al/g = 1.8 BTU), of organic materials is a measure of the heat released as the material burns. Calorimetry is the art of measuring quantities of heat. The procedures of oxygen bomb calorimetry involve the burning of a sample of known weight in a container, in the presence of oxygen. This container or "bomb" is submerged in a known quantity of water or is placed within a controlled atmosphere. As the sample in the bomb is ignited and burned, heat is released to the water or surrounding chamber. The change in water or air temperature is recorded and the caloric value of the sample may be determined. Samples as large as 1.0 gram, (10,000 calories) and as small as <0.1 gram, (100 calories) may be measured, depending upon the type of commercial instrument being used.

As an individual or ecosystem grows, increases in biomass ordinarily result in increases in the total number of calories of the system. At the same time the system may show an increase in the calories per gram of dry weight biomass. Changes in the caloric values may be of extreme ecological interest. Metabolic processes dictate the percentage of protein, carbohydrate and lipid present in a cell or system. Changes in these metabolic processes result in changes in the per cent of lipid, protein and carbohydrate which are then reflected as changes in the caloric values. Remember that lipids supply more than twice as many calories per gram as do proteins and carbohydrates. Increases in calories per gram and per cent carbon indicates that the system is increasing in the per cent lipids, also. Ecologists may be interested in changes in caloric values during succession of different ecosystems, during life cycles of various species or during the growth phase of pure or mixed cultures of microorganisms. Golley (1961) has compiled caloric value data for the benefit of ecologists.

The following procedure is based on information contained in Manuals 130 and 134, Parr Instrument Co., and by experience with Series 1200 Oxygen Bomb Calorimeter equipped with 2601 adiabetic control system.[1]

The Use of the Bomb Calorimeter

PROCEDURE

    I. Preparation of solid samples for combustion

        1. Solid sample material may be air-dried and ground to a particle size which will pass through a 60 mesh screen. Larger particles may not combust completely and smaller particles may be blown out of the combustion capsule by gases.

        2. Weigh less than 1.0 gm sample and press into a pellet. *Total weight of pellet should not exceed 1.0 gm.* If powdered sample will not remain compressed into a pellet add a *known quantity* of benzoic acid and mix with sample; pellet should now retain its form. Total caloric value of the pellet must be less than 10,000 calories (less than 1.10 gram).

---

1. By permission of Parr Instrument Co., 211 Fifty-Third Street, Moline, Illinois.

II. Preparation of liquid samples
1. Volatile liquids may be burned in gelatin capsules, in soft glass ampoules or in volatile sample holders. The volatile sample amount should be determined empirically and small sized samples used, i.e. less than 10,000 calories.
2. Instructions for firing volatile samples are given in Manual No. 130 of Parr Instrument Co., and vary according to sample and sample holder.

III. Loading, assembling and pressurizing the bomb
1. Set bomb head on support stand. Measure platinum fuse wire, 10-12 cm. Tie wire as shown in instruction manual.
2. Place sample pellet in cup; place cup in holder, and bend wire to contact the pellet.
3. Pipet 1.0 ml H_2O into bottom of bomb. Place bomb head carefully on bomb as it stands in bench clamp; tighten clamp and screw bomb head on carefully; tighten by hand.
4. Remove the small round knob from the top of the bomb and place the proper hose fitting from the O_2 valve in its place. Screw this fitting tightly *by hand*.
5. Slowly add O_2 up to 30 atmospheres pressure. Never add more than 35 atmospheres. (If more is added, do not combust! Release the O_2 pressure; open the bomb; check the sample and wire; reassemble the bomb and begin again.) Release pressure; remove hose; and replace knob.
6. Add 1 liter of distilled H_2O to calorimeter bucket; place bomb in bucket and connect the wire lead to the bomb. Place the bucket and bomb in the calorimeter, carefully. Add 1 liter distilled H_2O to make a total of 2 liters of H_2O in the bucket.
7. Lower the top of the jacket on the top of the calorimeter. This jacket must be lowered carefully to avoid damage to the thermometers. Check the pulley axles on the jacket top to see that they are engaged in order to circulate the water inside the jacket.
8. Lower thermometers into the jacket carefully, after making certain that thermisters are correctly attached. The thermometers should be turned to a position in which both may be read at the same time.

IV. Temperature adjustments and firing
1. Start the motor. Turn on calorimeter controller. Make certain jacket stirrers are operating correctly.
2. Allow the temperatures of the jacket and bucket to attain equilibrium. (Five minutes should be adequate.) At the end of this time adjust the temperatures to hold $\pm 0.01°F$ for 3 minutes.
3. Read and record the temperature of the calorimeter bucket to the nearest .002°F.
4. *FIRE* the charge by pressing the button on the ignition unit; release the button within 5 seconds. Within 20-30 seconds from firing the calorimeter temperature should begin to rise.
5. Take temperature reading at 1 minute intervals. The maximum temperature should be reached within 10 minutes; to assure that T max has been attained continue the readings until the same temperature is observed for 3 successive readings.
6. During steps 4 and 5, the calorimeter control should automatically maintain a temperature in the jacket comparable to that of the water in the bucket by adding hot and cold water when necessary.
7. Turn off controller. Lift thermometers. Remove jacket lid to side. Extract bucket and contents.
8. Take out bomb and let out internal pressure slowly with lever.
9. Empty and dry bucket.

10. Remove cup, wire, etc. Rinse all internal parts of bomb into a beaker or Erlenmeyer flask. Add Methyl Red indicator and titrate with .0725 N Na_2CO_3 (made by adding 3.84 gm Na_2CO_3 per liter of H_2O).
11. Measure wire and record.
12. Leave all equipment clean and dry.
13. Calculate results; see formula below.

Calculations for Adiabatic Calorimeter

Assembly of Data

The following data should be available at the completion of a test in the adiabetic calorimeter:

t_a = temperature at time of firing, corrected for thermometer scale error.

t_t = final maximum temperature, corrected for thermometer scale error.

c_1 = milliliters of standard alkali solution used in acid titration.

c_2 = percentage of sulfur in sample.

c_3 = centimeters of fuse wire consumed in firing.

W = energy equivalent of calorimeter in calories per degree Fahrenheit or Centigrade.

m = mass of sample in grams.

Temperature Rise

Compute the net corrected temperature rise, t, by substituting in the following equation:

$$t = t_t - t_a$$

Thermochemical Corrections

Compute the following for each test:

e_1 = correction in calories for heat of formation of nitric acid (HNO_3).

= c_1 if .0725 N alkali was used for the acid titration.

e_2 = correction in calories for heat of formation of sulfuric acid (H_2SO_4).

= $(14)(c_2)(m)$.

e_3 = correction in calories for heat of combustion of fuse wire.

= $(2.3)(c_3)$ when using Parr 45C10 nickel-chromium fuse wire, or

= $(2.7)(c_3)$ when using 34 B & X gage iron fuse wire.

Gross Heat of Combustion

Compute the gross heat of combustion, H_g, in calories per gram, by substitution in the following equation:

$$H_g = \frac{tW - e_1 - e_2 - e_3}{m}$$

Example

t_a = 76.910 − .001 = 76.909° F

t_t = 82.740 + .012 = 82.752° F

c_1 = 24.2 ml

c_2 = 1.04% S

c_3 = 7.4 cm Parr 45C10 wire

W = 1356 calories per deg. F

m = 0.9952 gram

t = 82.752 − 76.909

= 5.843° F

e_1 = 24.2 calories

e_2 = (14) (1.04) (.9952) = 14.5 calories

e_3 = (2.3) (7.4) = 17.0 calories

$$H_g = \frac{(5.843)(1356) - 24.2 - 14.5 - 17.0}{0.9952}$$

= 7905.3 calories per gram, or

= (7905.3) (1.8) = 14230 Btu. per pound

154

Operator _____ Sample No. _____

Date _____ Date of collection _____

Contents of sample _____

W = _____

_____ Capsule + sample

_____ Capsule

_____ Sample

_____ Capsule + ash

_____ Ash

m _____ Ash free dry weight of sample

_____ Final bucket temperature

_____ Thermometer correction

_____ Corrected final temperature

_____ Initial temperature

_____ Thermometer correction

_____ Corrected initial temperature

t _____ Temperature differential

e_1 _____ ml standard alkali used in titration

_____ % sulfur in sample

e_2 _____ Sulfur correction = (14) (m) (%S)

_____ cm fuse wire consumed

e_3 _____ Fuse wire correction = (cm consumed) (2.3)

Gross heat of combustion:

$$\frac{tW - e_1 - e_2 - e_3}{m}$$

155

Seawater in the Laboratory

Students using the manual may wish to use seawater rather than freshwater in certain experiments. Seawater may be available in some areas although many do not have ready access to a source. A few comments and cautions are in order.

1. Seawater may vary considerably in pH, salinity and organic carbon content.
2. Fresh seawater may contain substances which inhibit the growth of marine bacteria. It is often advisable to "age" the seawater by placing it in the dark, in a carboy or flask for a few weeks or months. Toxic substances are apparently degraded, partially by bacterial action, during this period.
3. Seawater may support the growth of certain microorganisms upon first isolation, after which they are unable to grow in seawater in the lab.
4. Concentrations of vitamins such as thiamin and biotin are ordinarily greater near the shore and the surface than in deep water.
5. Artificial seawater may support the growth of certain microorganisms while excluding others.
6. Artificial seawater may prove valuable in the laboratory (a) if it is the only source, (b) if a consistent, reliable seawater is required, or (c) if the nearby sources are polluted or otherwise unavailable.

Kester et al. (1968) have developed a formula for seawater which is consistent with the most recent analyses of natural seawater, salinity 35.00%. Table 5 lists the concentrations of the salts.

Table 5. Formula for 1 kg of 35.00% Artificial Seawater

A. Gravimetric salts

Salt	Molecular weight	G/kg of solution
NaCl	58.44	23.926
Na_2SO_4	142.04	4.008
KCl	74.56	0.677
$NaHCO_3$	84.00	0.196
KBr	119.01	0.098
H_3BO_3	61.83	0.026
NaF	41.99	0.003

B. Volumetric salts

Salt	Molecular weight	Moles/kg of solution	Conen	Stock Solution Density (23 C)
$MgCl_2 \cdot 6H_2O$	203.33	0.05327	1.0 M	1.071 g/ml
$CaCl_2 \cdot 2H_2O$	147.03	0.01033	1.0 M	1.085 g/ml
$SrCl_2 \cdot 6H_2O$	266.64	0.00009	0.1 M	1.013 g/ml

C. Distilled water to 1,000.000 g

Use reagent grade salts.

MATERIALS AND EQUIPMENT
Per group
  Flasks—2 liter and 1 liter, 1 each—500 ml, 3 each
  Reagent grade salts—see Table 1
  Semimicro-balance
  Magnetic stirrer—stirring bar or glass stirring rods

PROCEDURE
1. Two factors must be considered in the preparation:
   a. The reagents used must be weighable and of known composition.
   b. Salts must be added in such a way as to avoid precipitation of insoluble compounds.
2. Dry and weigh the following salts:
   $NaCl$, Na_2SO_4, KCl, KBr, NaF.
3. The composition of $NaHCO_3$ and H_3BO_3 may be changed by drying. Weigh without drying.
4. Water of hydration in these salts make weighing impractical; $MgCl_2$, $CaCl_2$ and $SrCl_2$. Prepare molar solutions of $MgCl_2 \cdot 6H_2O$ and $CaCl_2 \cdot 2H_2O$.
   a. Prepare a 0.1 molar solution of $SrCl_2 \cdot 6H_2O$. It may be necessary to filter insoluble materials from the $MgCl_2$ solution.
5. Prepare the seawater in two separate containers as directed here.
   a. In container 1 place all the salts from the gravimetric section; add in 2/3 of the total required H_2O volumetrically.
   b. To container 2 add the required amounts of the volumetric salts and 1/3 of the total required H_2O by volume.
   c. Mix these solutions thoroughly.
6. Combine the contents of the two containers while stirring constantly.
7. Aerate the seawater by drawing laboratory air through the flask until the pH changes no more than 0.02 units over a 2 hour period. Final pH after aeration will be about 8.2.
8. The pH may change during storage in the laboratory. Check the pH prior to use.
9. If the water is stored for a period of time, growth of microorganisms may appear on the surface. Storage in a cold room should prevent this. Carbon content of the water and the availability of light will influence the kind and amount of growth.
10. You may wish to compare this recipe with those of Riley and Skirrow (1965), Lyman and Fleming (1940) and with the composition of natural seawater.

Oxygen Determinations

The dissolved oxygen in an aquatic ecosystem is one of the factors directly influencing the numbers and types of organisms which can survive there. Water temperature and chemical water quality, as well as biological factors, are the main factors responsible for the availability of O_2. Dissolved O_2 is one of a number of routine measurements made by limnologists, sanitary engineers and others studying aquatic habitats.

The Winkler method was one of the first successful methods for measuring dissolved O_2 (D.O.) and works quite well in relatively pure waters containing fairly high concentrations of D.O. Nitrites, ferrous salts, organic matter, sulfites and other substances interfere with the accuracy of the Winkler method, causing errors in the determinations. Modifications of the original procedure have been made to overcome these causes of interference.[1]

A brief description of the basic Winkler method and a stepwise procedure are presented here:

Winkler Method

$$MnSO_4 + 2 KOH \rightarrow Mn(OH)_2 + K_2SO_4$$

1. *Fill* BOD bottle with 300 ml of sample; run over 2-3 times if possible—do not bubble in.
2. Add 2 ml $MnSO_4$.
3. Add 2 ml Na Azide (Alkali Iodide Azide Solution).
4. Shake and let settle until 100 ml of coagulant settle out.
5. Add 2 ml of concentrated H_2SO_4, letting it run down the neck of the bottle; restopper, and mix by gentle inversion until dissolution is complete.
6. Titrate 80 ml of sample with .01 N Sodium Thiosulfate, using 1 ml of freshly prepared starch as indicator.
7. Ml of Titrant used = ppm of D.O.

If a white ppt. if obtained, there is no dissolved oxygen in the sample. A brown precipitate shows that oxygen is present.

$$2 Mn(OH)_2 + O_2 \rightarrow 2 MnO(OH)_2$$

$$MnO(OH)_2 + 2 H_5SO_4 \rightarrow Mn(SO_4)_2 + 3 H_2O$$

$$Mn(SO_4)_2 + 2 KI \rightarrow MnSO_4 + K_2SO_4 + I_2$$

$$2 Na_2S_2O_3 + I_2 \rightarrow Na_2S_4O_6 + 2 NaI$$

The Winkler method and modifications are acceptable for laboratory determinations and are standard procedure in water treatment laboratories.[2] Various types of probes and electrodes have been developed for measuring the D.O. in rivers, lakes and the seas. These probles are ordinarily attached to cords or cables which allow them to be suspended at the desired depth while the reading is made at the surface. Since the saturation constant of D.O. in the water is related to water temperature, D.O. probes commonly have a thermometer or temperature compensating device incorporated in the probe. Most probes of this type are Clark-type electrodes which depend upon a flow of liquid past the probe

---

1. The Winkler method and modifications are thoroughly discussed in Standard Methods for the examination of water and sewage, American Public Health Association and in other publications.
2. Ibid.

since the O_2 is depleted in front of the probe membrane. In flowing water no movement of the probe is required but an up and down movement is necessary in standing water. In the laboratory a magnetic stirrer gently agitating the water is sufficient. If an oxygen electrode is available consult the instruction manual so that best results may be obtained.

Microbial ecologists often have reason to measure oxygen at low concentrations. The Winkler method is imprecise at D.O. concentrations below 10% of the saturation value. At these very low concentrations special handling methods are required to avoid atmospheric contamination of the sample. Broenkow and Cline (1969) have developed a method which employs sampling syringes and reagents similar to the Winkler reagents (although at 0.1 the concentration) which is precise at these low concentrations. The procedure is designed to supplement the Winkler method rather than replace it and is available in the above paper and will not be repeated here.

Recommended Readings

Alexander, M. 1961. *Introduction to soil microbiology.* New York: John Wiley & Sons, Inc., 472 p.

American Public Health Association. *Standard methods for the examination of water and wastewater.* 12th edition.

Baker, K. F. and W. C. Snyder. 1965. *Ecology of soil-borne plant pathogens.* Berkeley: U. of California Press, 571 p.

Brock, M. L. and T. D. Brock. 1968. The application of microautoradiographic techniques to ecological studies. *Mitt. internat. Verein. Limnol.* 15:1-29.

Clarke, F. E. 1965. The concept of competition in microbial ecology. In K. F. Baker and W. C. Snyder, eds. *Ecology of soil-borne plant pathogens.* Berkeley: U. of California Press, p. 339-347.

Collins, C. H. 1967. *Progress in microbiological techniques.* New York: Plenum Press, 231 p.

Davis, J. B. 1967. *Petroleum microbiology.* New York: Elsevier Publ. Co., 604 p.

Droop, M. R. and E. J. F. Wood. 1968. *Advances in microbiology of the sea.* London: I. Academic Press, 239 p.

Gray, T. R. G. and D. Parkinson. 1968. *The ecology of soil bacteria.* An International Symposium. Toronto: U. of Toronto Press, 681 p.

Hynes, H. B. N. 1960. *The biology of polluted waters.* Liverpool U. Press, 202 p.

Krasilnikov, N. A. 1958. *Soil microorganisms and higher plants.* Moscow: Acad. of Sciences in U.S.S.R., Moscow, 474 p.

Malek, I. and Z Fencl. 1966. *Theoretical and methodological basis of continuous culture of microorganisms.* New York: Academic Press, Inc., 655 p.

Marples, M. J. 1965. *The ecology of the human skin.* Springfield, Ill.: Charles C. Thomas Publ., 970 p.

Riley, J. P. and G. Skirrow. 1965. *Chemical oceanography.* London: I. Academic, 712 p.

Steinhaus, E. A. 1967. *Insect microbiology.* New York: Hafner Publ. Co., Inc., 763 p.

Strickland, J. D. H. and T. R. Parsons. 1965. *A manual of sea water analysis.* Bull. Fisheries Res. Board Can. 125, 2nd edition, 203 p.

Zobell, C. E. 1946. Marine microbiology. Waltham, Mass.: Chronica Botonica Co., 240 p.

References

Aaronson, S. 1970. *Experimental microbial ecology*. New York: Academic Press Inc., 236 p.

Abbott, W. 1966. Microcosm studies on estuarine waters I. The replicability of microcosms. *J. Water Poll. Cont. Feder.* 38:258-270.

Alexander, M. 1964. Biochemical ecology of soil microorganisms. *Ann. Rev. Microbiol.* 18:217-252.

Allen, H. L. 1968. Acetate in freshwater: natural substrate concentrations determined by dilution bioassay. *Ecology* 49:346-349.

Allen, S. D. and T. D. Brock. 1968. The adaptation of heterotrophic microcosms to different temperatures. *Ecology* 49:343-346.

Baas Becking, L. G. M.; E. J. F. Wood; and I. R. Kaplan. 1957. Biological process in the estuarine environment, X', Kon. Ned. Akad. Weten. Proc., B60, 88-102.

Bauman, P. 1968. Isolation of *Acinetobacter* from soil and water. *J. Bacteriol.* 96:39-42.

Beyers, R. J. 1963. The metabolism of twelve aquatic laboratory microecosystems. *Ecol. Monogr.* 33:281-306.

———. 1964. The microcosm approach to ecosystem biology. *The Amer. Biol. Teacher* 26:491-498.

Beyers, R. J.; J. L. Larimer; H. T. Odum; R. B. Parker; and N. E. Armstrong. 1963. Directions for the determination of changes in carbon dioxide concentration from changes in *p*H. *Publ. Inst. Marine Science* 9:454-489.

Beyers, R. J. and H. T. Odum. 1959. The use of carbon dioxide to construct *p*H curves for the measurement of productivity. *Limnol. Oceanogr.* 4:499-502.

Brock, T. D. 1967a. Bacterial growth rate in the sea: direct analysis by thymidine autoradiography. *Science* 155:81-83.

———. 1967b. The ecosystem and the steady state. *BioScience* 17:166-169.

Brock, T. D. and M. L. Brock. 1966. Autoradiography as a tool in microbial ecology. *Nature* 209:734-736.

———. 1968. Measurement of steady-state growth rates of a thermophilic alga directly in nature. *J. Bacteriol.* 95:811-815.

Broenkow, W. W. and J. D. Cline. 1969. Colorimetric determinations of dissolved oxygen at low concentrations. *Limnol. Oceanogr.* 14:450-454.

Carpenter, E. J. 1968. A simple, inexpensive algal chemostat. *Limnol. Oceanogr.* 13:720-721.

Chappelle, E. W. and G. V. Levin. 1968. Use of the firefly bioluminescent reaction for rapid detection and counting of bacteria. *Biochem. Med.* 2:41-52.

Contois, D. E. 1959. Kinetics of bacterial growth: relationship between population density and specific growth rate of continuous cultures. *J. Gen. Microbiol.* 21:40-50.

Cooke, D. 1967. The pattern of autotrophic succession in laboratory microcosms. *BioScience* 17:717-722.

———. 1969. Aquatic laboratory microecosystems and communities. In David Clark ed. *The structure and function of aquatic microbial communities*. VPI Press. in press.

Cooke, D., R. J. Beyers and E. P. Odum. 1968. The case for the multi-species ecological system, with special reference to succession and stability. In J. F. Saunders ed. *Bioregenerative systems.* NASA SP-165:129-139.

Crossley, D. A. and M. P. Hoglund. 1962. A litter-bag method for the study of microarthropods inhabiting leaf litter. *Ecology* 43:571-574.

Dobson, A. N. and W. H. Thomas. 1964. Concentrating plankton in a gentle fashion. *Limnol. Oceanogr.* 9:455-456.

Donald, C. M. 1960. The impact of cheap nitrogen. *Aust. Inst. Agr. Sci. J.* 26:319-338.

Englemann, M. D. 1961. The role of soil arthropods in the energetics of an old field community. *Ecol. Monogr.* 31:221-238.

Gaudy, A. F. Jr. and Elizabeth T. Gaudy. 1966. Microbiology of waste waters. *Ann. Rev. Microbiol.* 20:319-336.

Goldman, C. R. 1963. The measurement of productivity and limiting factors in freshwater with carbon-14. In M. S. Doty (ed.), Proceedings of the conference on primary productivity measurement, marine and freshwater. U.S. Atomic Energy Comm. Div. Tech. Inform. rep. TID-7633, 103-113.

Golley, F. B. 1961. Energy values of ecological materials. *Ecology* 42:581-584.

Gorden, R. W. 1969. A proposed energy budget of a soybean field. *Bulletin Georgia Acad. Sci.* 27:41-52.

Gorden, R. W., R. J. Beyers; E. P. Odum; and R. G. Eagon. 1969. Studies of a simple laboratory microecosystem: bacterial activities in a heterotrophic succession. *Ecology* 50:86-100.

Gray, F. V., R. A. Weller; and G. B. Jones. 1965. The rates of production of volatile fatty acids in the rumen II. Measurement of the production in an artificial rumen and application of the isotope dilution technique to the rumen of a sheep. *Aust. J. Agr. Res.* 16:145-157.

Harwood, J. E.; R. A. von Steenderen; and A. L. Kuhn. 1969a. A rapid method for orthophosphate analysis at high concentrations in water. *Water Res. 3:417-423.*

———. 1969b. A comparison of some methods for total phosphate analysis. *Water Res.* 3:425-432.

Hasler, A. D. 1969. Cultural eutrophication is reversible. *BioScience* 19:425-431.

Hayes, F. R. and J. E. Phillips. 1958. Lake water and sediment. IV. Radiophosphorus equilibrium with mud, plants, and bacteria under oxidized and reduced conditions. *Limnol. Oceanogr.* 3:459-475.

Herbert, D.; R. Elsworth; and R. C. Telling. 1956. The continuous culture of bacteria; a theoretical and experimental study. *J. Gen. Microbiol.* 14:601-622.

Hobbie, J. E. and C. C. Crawford. 1969. Respiration corrections for bacterial uptake of dissolved organic compounds in natural waters. *Limnol. Oceanogr.* 14:528-532.

Hobbie, J. E. and R. T. Wright. 1965. Bioassay with bacterial uptake kinetics: glucose in freshwater. *Limnol. Oceanogr.* 10:471-474.

Holm-Hansen, O. and C. R. Booth. 1966. The measurement of adenosine triphosphate in the ocean and its ecological significance. *Limnol. Oceanogr.* 11:510-519.

Hungate, R. E. 1966. *The rumen and its microbes.* New York: Academic Press Inc., 533 p.

Hutchinson, G. Evelyn. 1967. *A treatise on limnology, II: introduction to lake biology and the limnoplankton.* New York: John Wiley & Sons, Inc., 1115 p.

Jankovic, S. G.; D. T. Mitchell; and J. C. Buzzell, Jr. 1967. Measurement of phosphorus in wastewater. *Water and Sew. Wks.* 114:471-475.

Jannasch, H. W. 1962. Studies on the ecology of a marine spirillum in the chemostat. 1st Int. Sympos. Mar. Microbiol. Thomas, Springfield, Ill. p. 558-566.

———. 1964. Microbial decomposition in natural waters as determined in steady state systems. *Verb. Internat. Verein. Limnol.* 15:562-568.

———. 1965. Continuous culture in microbial ecology. *Lab. Pract.* 1162-1167.

Javornicky, P. and Vera Prokesora. 1963. The influence of protozoa and bacteria upon the oxidation of organic substances in water. *Int. Revue ges. Hydrobio.* 48:335-350.

Johannes, R. E. 1965. Influence of marine protozoa on nutrient regeneration. *Limnol. Oceanogr.* 10:434-442.

Johannes, R. E. and S. Masako. 1966. Composition and nutritive value of fecal pellets of a marine crustacean. *Limnol. Oceanogr.* 11:191-197.

Kester, D. R.; I. W. Duedall, D. R. Connors; and R. M. Pytkowica. 1968. Preparation of artificial seawater. *Limnol. Oceanogr.* 12:176-178.

Kimball, J. F. Jr. and E. J. F. Wood. 1964. A simple centrifuge for phytoplankton studies. *Bull. Mar. Sci. Gulf Caribbean* 14:539-544.

Knowles, R. 1965. The significance of nonsymbiotic nitrogen fixation. *Soil Sci. Soc. Amer. Proc.* 29:223.

Lederberg, J. and E. M. Lederberg. 1952. Replica plating and indirect selection of bacterial mutants. *J. Bacteriol.* 63:399-406.

Lee, G. F. and A. W. Hoadley. 1967. Biological activity in relation to the chemical equilibrium composition of natural waters. In R. F. Gould (ed.), *Equilibrium concepts in natural water systems.* Adv. in Chem. Series 67. American Chemical Society Publications.

Leo, R. F. and P. L. Parker. 1966. Branched-chain fatty acids in sediments. *Science* 152:649-650.

Likens, G. E.; F. H. Bormann; N. M. Johnson; and R. S. Pierce. 1967. The calcium, magnesium, potassium, and sodium budgets for a small forested ecosystem. *Ecology* 48:772-785.

Lind, O. and R. S. Campbell. 1969. Comments on the use of liquid scintillation for routine determination of ^{14}C activity in production studies. *Limnol. Oceanog.* 14:787-789.

Lorenzen, C. J. 1967. Determination of chlorophyll and pheo-pigments: spectrometric equations. *Limnol. Oceanogr.* 12:343-346.

Lyman, J. and R. H. Fleming. 1940. Composition of seawater. *J. Mar. Res.* 3:134-146.

MacLeod, N. H.; E. W. Chappelle; and A. M. Crawford. 1962. ATP assay of terrestrial soils: a test of an exobiological experiment. *Nature,* 223:267-268.

Malek, J., K. Beran, and J. Hospodka. 1964. *Continuous culture of microorganisms; proceedings of the second symposium.* New York: Academic Press Inc., 391 p.

Margalef, R. 1963a. On certain unifying principles in ecology. *Amer. Nat.* 98:357-374.

———. 1963b. Successions of marine populations. *Adv. Frontiers Plant Science* 2:137-188.

Marples, M. J. 1969. Life on the human skin. *Sci. Amer.* 220:108-115.

McIntire, C. D. 1968. Structural characteristics of benthic algal communities in laboratory streams. *Ecology* 49:520-537.

Meyers, S. P. and B. E. Hopper. 1966. Attraction of the marine nematode, *Metoncholaimus* sp. to fungal substrates. *Bull. Mar. Sci.* 16:142-150.

Moss, B. 1967a. A spectrophotometric method for the estimation of percentage degradation of chlorophylls to pheo-pigments in extract of algae. *Limnol. Oceanogr.* 12:335-340.

———. 1967b. A note on the estimation of chlorophyll *a* in freshwater algae communities. *Limnol. Oceanogr.* 12:340-342.

Murphy, J. and J. P. Riley. 1962. A modified single solution method for the determination of phosphate in natural waters. *Anal. Chem. Acta.* 27:31-36.

Odum, E. P. 1959. Fundamentals of ecology. 2nd Ed. Saunders, Phila. 546 p.

———. 1969. The strategy of ecosystem development. *Science* 164:262-270.

Odum, E. P. and E. J. Kuenzler. 1963. Experimental isolation of food-chains in an old-field ecosystem with the use of phosphorus-32. In V. Schultz and A. W. Klement, Jr. eds. *Radioecology.* New York: Reinhold Publ. Corp., p. 113-120.

Odum, H. T. 1957. Trophic structure and productivity of Silver Springs, Florida. *Ecol. Monogr.* 27:55-112.

Olson, J. S. 1968. Use of tracer techniques for the study of biogeochemical cycles. In F. E. Eckardt, ed. *Functioning of terrestrial ecosystems at the primary production level.* Paris, UNESCO, p. 271-288.

Parsons, T. R. and J. D. H. Strickland. 1961. On the production of particulate organic carbon by heterotrophic processes in seawater. *Deep Sea Research* 8:211-222.

———. 1963. Discussion of spectrophotometric determination of marine-plant pigments, with revised equations for ascertaining chlorophylls and carotenoids. *J. Mar. Res.* 21:155-163.

Patterson, J. W.; P. L. Brezonik; and H. D. Putnam. 1970. Measurement and significance of adenosine triphosphate in activated sludge. *Environ. Sci. Tech.* 4:569-575.

Powell, E. O. 1956. Growth rate and generation time of bacteria, with special reference to continuous culture. *J. Gen. Microbiol.* 15:492-511.

Reiners, W. A. 1968. Carbon dioxide evolution from the floor of three Minnesota forests. *Ecology* 49:471-483.

Riley, J. P. and G. Skirrow. 1965. *Chemical oceanography.* London: I. Academic Press, 712 p.

Riva, H. L. and T. R. Turner. 1962. Fluorescence microscopy in exfoliative cytology. *Obstetrics and Gynecology* 20:451-457.

Rogers, A. W. 1967. *Techniques of autoradiography.* New York: Elsevier Publ. Co., 335 p.

Seliger, H. H. and W. D. McElroy. 1960. Spectral emission and quantum yield of firefly bioluminescence. *Arch. Biochem. Biophys.* 88:136-141.

Sorokin, Y. I. 1965. On the trophic role of chemosynthesis and bacterial biosynthesis in water bodies. In C. R. Goldman, ed. Primary productivity in aquatic environments. Mem. Ist. Ital. Idrobiol., 18 Suppl., Berkeley: University of California Press, p. 187-205.

Stewart, W. D. P. 1966. Nitrogen fixation in plants. London: The Athlone Press, 168 p.

———. 1967. Nitrogen fixing plants. *Science* 158:1426-1431.

Stewart, W. D. P.; G. P. Fitzgerald; and R. H. Burris. 1967. *In situ* studies on N_2 fixation using acetylene reduction technique. *Proc. Nat. Acad. Sci.* U.S.A. 58:2071-2078.

Stewart, W. D. P. and M. C. Pearson. 1967. Nodulation and nitrogen-fixation by *Hippophae Rhamnoides L.* in the field. *Plant Soil* 26:348-360.

Strügger, S. 1948. Fluorescence microscope examination of bacteria in soil. *Cand. J. Res.* Sec. C., 26:188-193.

Vaccaro, R. F. and H. W. Jannasch. 1966. Studies on heterotrophic activity in seawater based on glucose assimilation. *Limnol. Oceanogr.* 11:596-607.

Westlake, D. F. 1965. Theoretical aspects of the comparability of productivity data. In C. R. Goldman (ed.), Primary productivity in aquatic environments. Mem. Ist. Ital. Idrobiol., 18 Suppl., Berkeley: University of California Press, p. 313-322.

Witkamp, M. 1963. Microbial populations of leaf litter in relation to environmental conditions and decomposition. *Ecology* 44:370-377.

———. 1966a. Decomposition of leaf litter in relation to environment, microflora, and microbial respiration. *Ecology* 47:194-201.

———. 1966b. Rates of CO_2 evolution from the forest floor. *Ecology* 47:492-494.

Witkamp, M. and J. S. Olson. 1963. Breakdown of confined and non-confined oak litter. *Oikos* 14:138-147.

Wood, E. J. F. 1964. Studies in microbial ecology of the Australasian Region. Nova Hedwigia VIII, 3/4:5-568.

———. 1965. *Marine Microbial Ecology.* New York: Reinhold Publ. Corp., 243 p.

Wood, H. G. and R. L. Stjernholm. 1962. Assimilation of carbon dioxide by heterotrophic organisms. In I. C. Gunsalus and R. Y. Stanier, eds. *The bacteria: a treatise on structure and function.* III:41-117.

Wright, R. T. and J. E. Hobbie. 1965. The uptake of organic solutes in lake water. *Limnol. Oceanogr.* 10:22-28.

———. 1966. Use of glucose and acetate by bacteria and algae in aquatic ecosystems. *Ecology* 47:447-464.

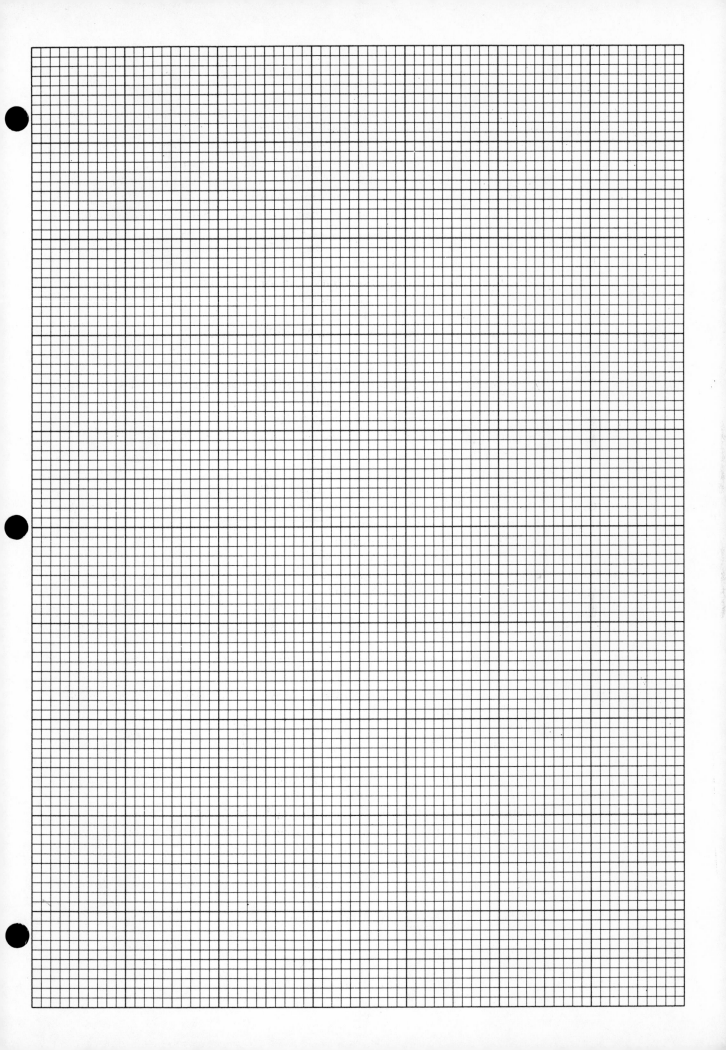

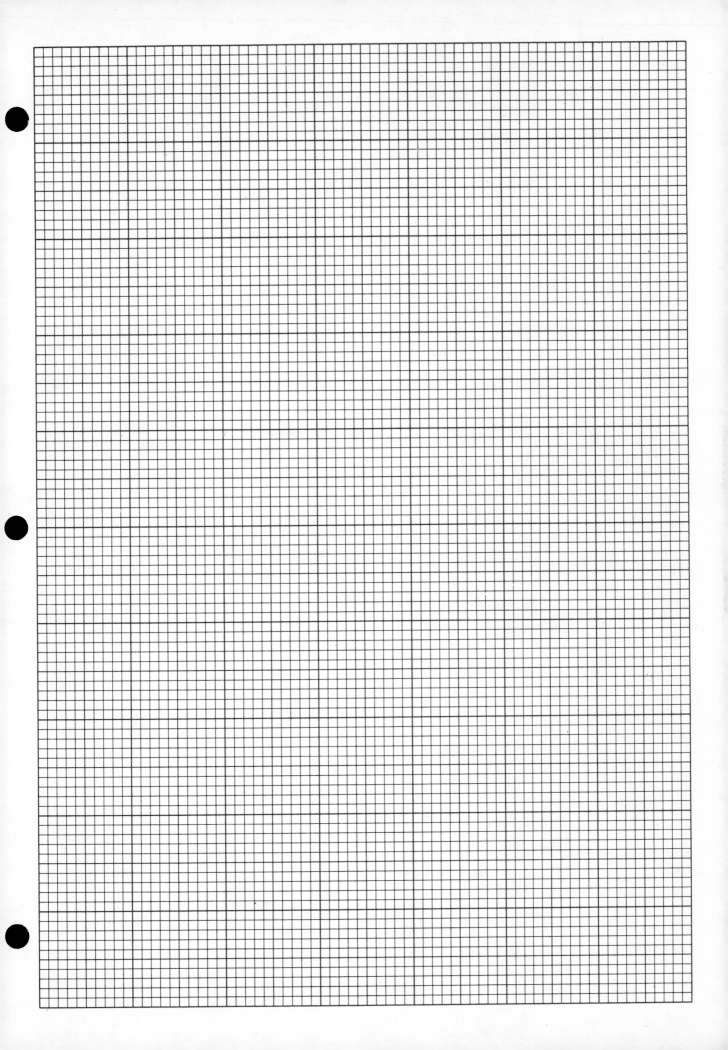

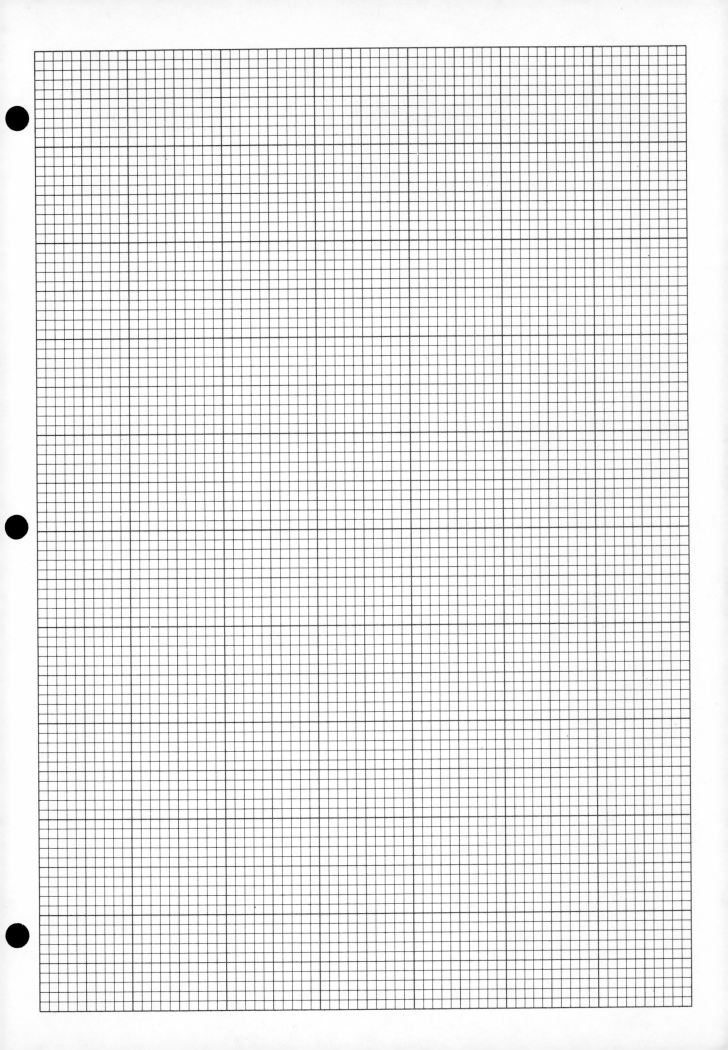

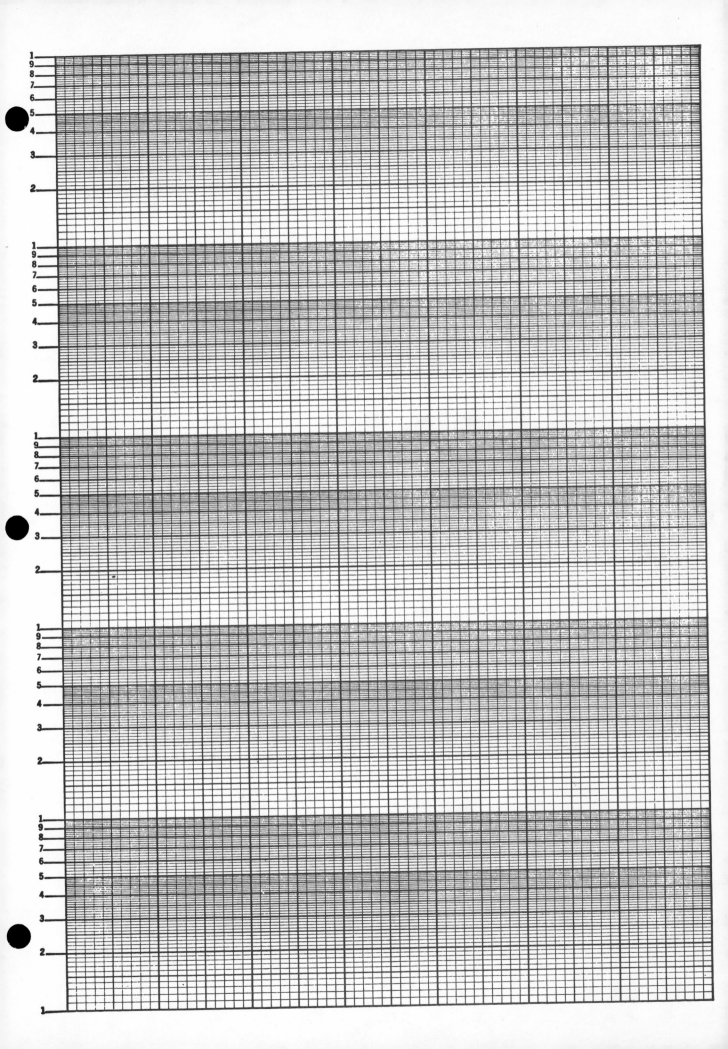

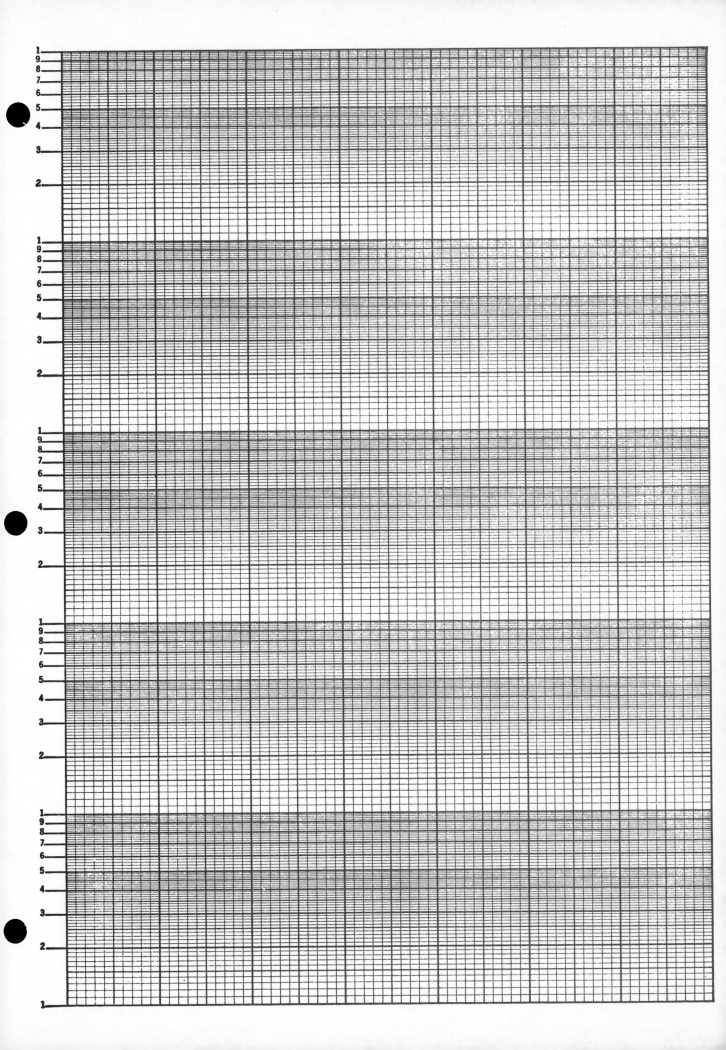

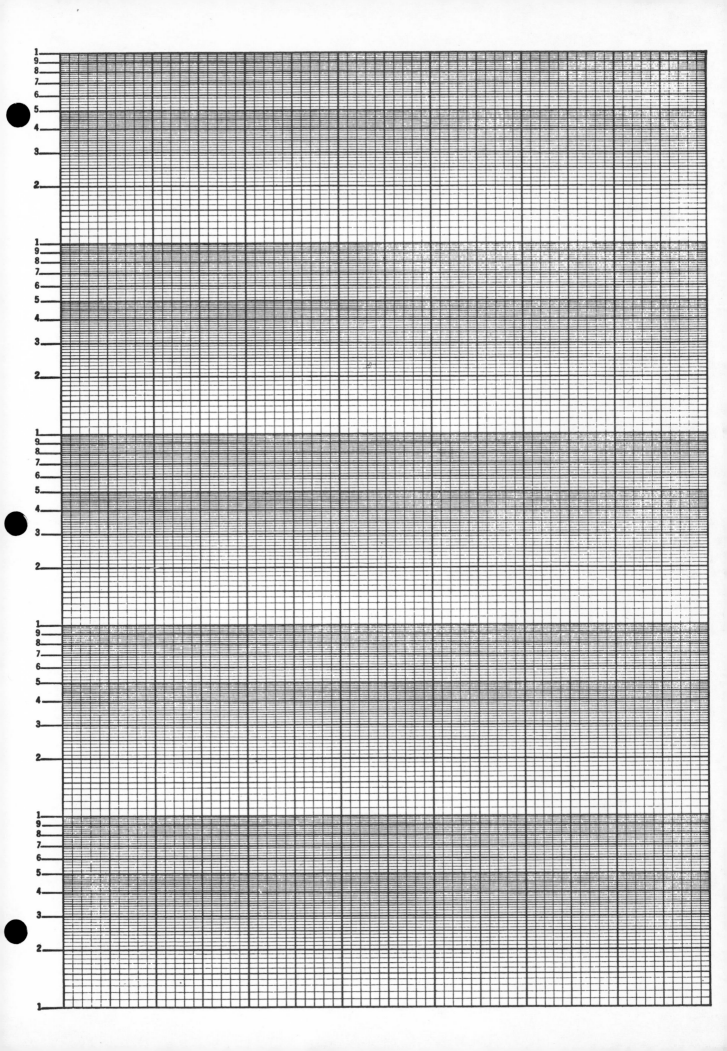

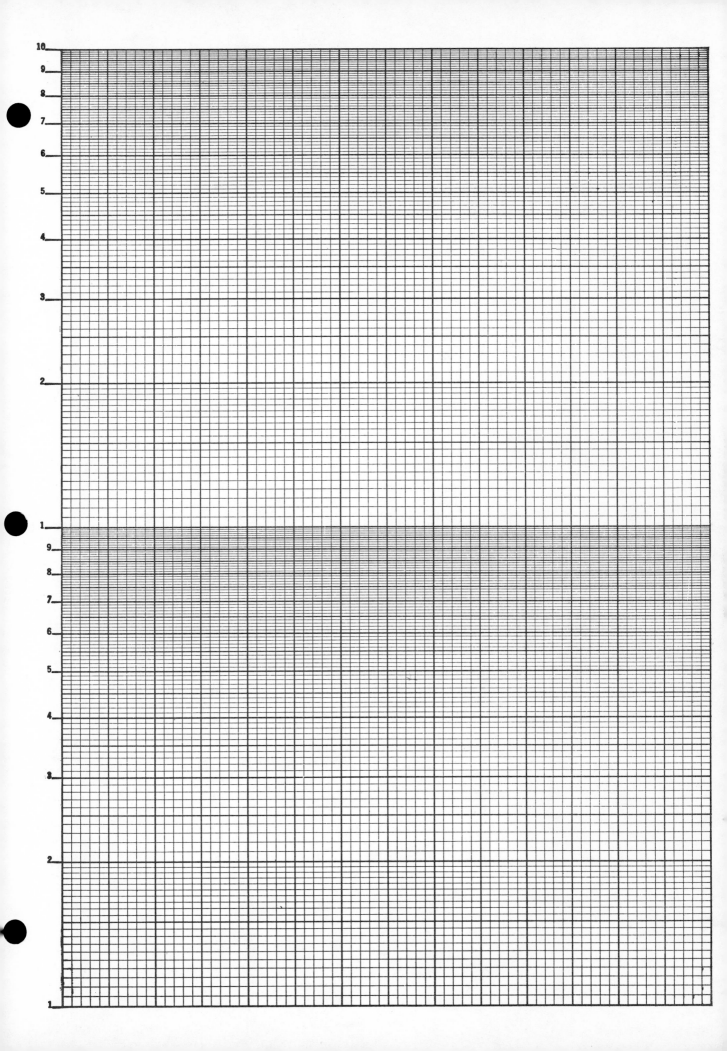

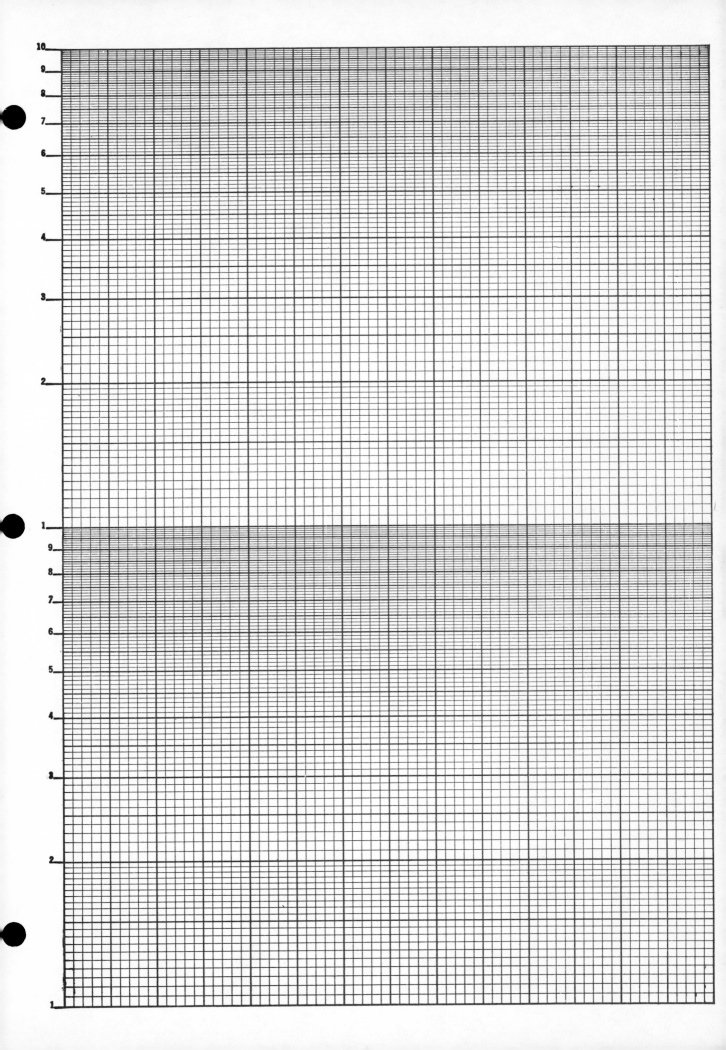

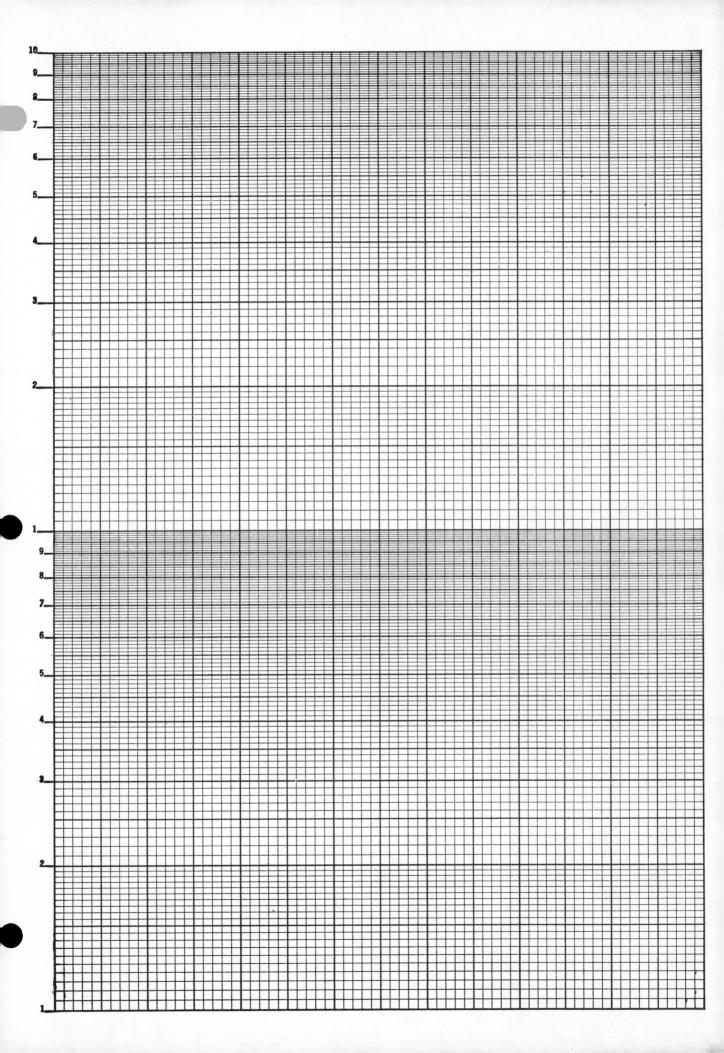